Historical [illegible] To Research And Perform

by

Nancy Polette

© 2002 Nancy Polette
Published by Pieces of Learning
Cover by John Steele
Graphic Design by Sharolyn Hill
www.piecesoflearning.com
CLC0280
ISBN 1-931334-14-5
Printed in the U.S.A.

HISTORICAL HOAXES TO RESEARCH AND PERFORM

CONTENTS

HISTORICAL HOAXES TO RESEARCH AND PERFORM

Do sea serpents and mermaids really exist? Did giants once wander the earth? Did Taco Bell® actually purchase the Liberty Bell? These and other fascinating questions are answered in *Historical Hoaxes to Research and Perform.*

Hoaxes have been a part of American history since the beginning of the nation. Among the most well-known hoaxters were Benjamin Franklin and Edgar Allen Poe. These and other men of letters enjoyed playing a good joke on a gullible public through newspaper and magazine articles and in books. It was often easy to trick readers who had been taught in school that anything in print must be true. How many times have students heard teachers say, "What does your book say? Look it up."

Each of the eleven plays is based on an actual incident in American History. Before performing the plays, students are asked to research specific information related to the time, place or persons involved. There are four to eight research tasks in each play.

Additional reading sources are given for students who want to find out more about American history and discover the truth behind the claims. The student who does the research reads his or her results at the appropriate point in the play.

In performing the play readers are usually arranged in a straight line facing the audience. They stand in the order in which they first speak. All readers carry and use scripts even if lines have been memorized although memorizing lines is NOT necessary. Readers who are not reading can look down or turn slightly away. When entering and taking their places on the

"stage" readers carry the script in the hand which is away from the audience.

In practice sessions the readers should work on clear speech and on projecting the voice so that all can hear. Expressive and energetic reading should be practiced.

The cast should enter the stage or readers' area from two sides with each side entering at the same time. Posture should be good and the readers might indicate through body language the mood of the piece or something about the characters (are they energetic, tired, happy, sad, scared etc.?)

Developing a well-researched and finished piece brings a feeling of pride and accomplishment as young thespians perform what they have learned. Stimulating an interest in American history and researching topics to create a meaningful product are the first steps in developing an appreciation and desire to know more about our country's heritage. **Historical Hoaxes to Research and Perform** is intended to help in meeting this goal.

1730 THE WITCH TRIAL AT MOUNT HOLLY

Reading Parts
Narrator, Janet, Arthur, Bailiff, Judge, Prosecutor, Defense, Martha Corey, Small child

NARRATOR The Witch Trials were supposed to have ended in 1693 after which jurors and magistrates apologized and restitution was made to the families of those hanged as witches. But was this really the last of the trials? More than 200 years later the question is still being asked. The scene is a middle school classroom.

JANET My report is on the Salem Witch Trials. In 1692, in Salem Village, Massachusetts, the minister's daughter, his niece and other village girls were taken with horrible fits. The doctor stated that the girls had been bewitched. Three village women were accused and jailed.

WRITER ONE By May of 1692 how many other villagers were jailed and accused of being witches? Did this number include only women or were men also accused? What was the punishment for one found guilty of witchcraft? When was the last witch trial held?

____

____

____

ARTHUR Hold it! Just one minute! You have the dates wrong. The last witch trial was held nearly forty years later in Mount Holly,

Pennsylvania. I have a print-out of the news article to prove it. See! *The Pennsylvania Gazette*, October 22, 1730.

JANET I don't believe it. Every source I read said there were no more trials after 1692.

ARTHUR The trial transcript is right here. Read it yourself.

NARRATOR The year is 1730. The place, Mount Holly, Pennsylvania. The scene is a courtroom.

BAILIFF Hear ye, hear ye, all who have business with the Court come forward. The Honorable Judge Jeramiah Peckworth presiding.

JUDGE The Bailiff will read the charges.

BAILIFF This man and this woman are accused of witchcraft.

JUDGE Prosecutor, call your first witness.

PROSECUTOR Will Martha Corey take the stand.

WRITER TWO Describe Martha Corey. How would she, as a typical Colonial woman, be dressed?

____

____

____

PROSECUTOR Mistress Corey, now that you are duly sworn will you tell the court what you saw and heard?

MARTHA It was dreadful. When those two witches walked by my farm my hogs began reciting Psalms. Can you imagine? I love the Psalms, but I was shocked to hear them coming from the snouts of my hogs! My neighbor, Penelope Purdy heard them, too. See, there she is on the front row holding her little boy and nodding her head.

PROSECUTOR Did anything else happen when the accused walked by your farm?

MARTHA I should say so! The sheep started dancing. Now you know dancing is not allowed in this province. It was disgraceful and enough to strike terror and amazement in every good and peaceable subject of Mount Holly, of which I am one.

JUDGE The defense may now cross-examine the witness.

DEFENSE Mistress Corey, you have made some serious accusations. Are you willing to put these so-called witches to the test?

MARTHA Certainly.

DEFENSE In addition, are you and Mistress Purdy willing to take the same tests?

MARTHA Of course. It is quite clear that neither of us is a witch. What tests do you propose?

WRITER THREE Research and report on traditional tests given to determine if a person was a witch.

____

____

____

NARRATOR The first test took place in the courtroom. A large scale was brought in. One at a time the accused and their accusers sat on one end of the scale. On the other end was a Bible. If the scale showed the person was heavier than the Bible, this was proof that he or she was not a witch.

MARTHA You see, the scale shows that both Penelope and I are heavier than the Bible, clear evidence that WE have nothing to do with witchcraft. Why even her little boy is heavier than the Bible.

DEFENSE The scale shows that each of the accused has also passed the test. I submit that this trial should be ended now.

JUDGE Your request is premature. We will proceed to the Mill Pond for the second test.

NARRATOR All four were bound and thrown into the Mill Pond. Those who did not sink were considered to be witches. The accused man who was very skinny sank at once. The three women bobbed on top of the water.

MARTHA The accused has bewitched us to make us so light that we float.

DEFENSE But look, the accused woman floats also. If she were truly a witch she could make herself sink.

SMALL CHILD I think their dresses look like balloons and that is why the ladies float and the man sinks.

JUDGE I do believe the child is right. Haul them out. This trial will be postponed until warmer weather when the ladies can wear lighter clothing.

ARTHUR You see, I was right. The trial WAS reported in *The Pennsylvania Gazette* exactly as it happened.

JANET Just because it's in a newspaper doesn't make it true.

NARRATOR How right Janet is! The so-called news story about the "Witch Trial at Mount Holly" was a hoax. Pennsylvanians read about it with great fascination and many believed every word. The editor, a very famous American who wrote the story, was making fun of those who still thought witches existed.

SUPER RESEARCH CHALLENGE

WRITER FOUR Find out the name of the editor of the *Pennsylvania Gazette* in 1730.
His name was ________________________. Tell about other hoaxes or jokes he was famous for.

____

____

____

____

____

____

____

____

____

____

____

THE WITCH TRIAL AT MOUNT HOLLY

ADDITIONAL READING

Encounters with the Invisible World by M.K. Roach. Crowell, 1977.
Tales of ghosts and witches in New England.

Tibuta of Salem Village by A. L. Petry. Crowell, 1964.
A slave becomes a central figure in a witchcraft trial.

Witchcraft of Salem Village by Shirley Jackson. Random House, 1987.
An account of the witchcraft trials of 1692-93 during which 20 people were put to death.

Witch Hunt by Stephen Krensky. Random House, 1989.
An account of the madness that overtook Salem Village.

Witch of Blackbird Pond by Elizabeth George Speare. Houghton-Mifflin, 1958.
A spirited young girl must adjust to life in a strict New England household.

Witches by C. Pike. Archway, 1997.
Tales about witches, spells and magic.

Witches and Witch-Hunts by Milton Meltzer. Scholastic, 1999.
The devastation witch hunts have caused throughout history.

The Witches of Worm by Zilpha K. Snyder. Atheneum, 1972.
A child is controlled by a force that makes her play harmful tricks.

The Witch's Eye by Phyllis Reynolds Naylor. Delacorte, 1990.
A glass eye of a suspected witch brings danger to a family.

Witch by C. Pike. Archway, 1990.
A young girl with supernatural powers tries to stop a murder that she foresees.

1730 THE WITCH TRIAL AT MOUNT HOLLY

Pennsylvania Gazette, October 22, 1730. pp. 3-4

Armstrong, Karen. **A Delusion of Satan: The Full Story of the Salem Witch Trials**. DeCapo Press, 1997.

Kallen, Stuart. **Salem Witch Trials, How History is Invented**. Lucent Books, 1999.

1730 THE GHOSTLY DRUMMER OF TEDWORTH

The ghostly drummer first appeared in 1661 in England and resurfaced in Philadelphia in 1730, frightening two respected clergymen.

Reading Parts Reverend Wright, Reverend Low, The Drummer, Narrator, Reverend True, Mrs. Wright

REVEREND WRIGHT Perhaps, Brother Low, a small glass of wine would be an appropriate end to a most enlightening day.

REVEREND LOW Indeed, Brother Wright, my head is quite swimming with ideas. We must keep up with modern times, you know. I heard today that the very first library will open in Philadelphia in a year's time. What a font of information that will be!

WRITER ONE Tell who established the first library in Philadelphia. What were other "firsts" attributed to this person?

___

___

___

___

NARRATOR The two clergymen had been attending a meeting of ministers in Philadelphia. They were sharing a room and after retiring were soon sound asleep.

GHOST DRUMMER Thump, thump, thump, thump, thump, Thump, thump, thump,

REVEREND WRIGHT Brother Low, wake up. Do you hear it?

REVEREND LOW Yes, it's beating on the side of the bed. Quick, light the candle!

REVEREND WRIGHT It's drumming out the 'Grenadiers March.'

REVEREND LOW And it's not a whit less obstreperous than the Tedworth Drummer.

REVEREND WRIGHT Surely you don't believe that foolish tale.

WRITER TWO Tell the tale of "The Ghostly Drummer of Tedworth." One good source on the internet is http://www.museumofhoaxes.com/tedworth.html

____

____

____

____

____

REVEREND LOW Foolish or not, there are many who do believe it. But it is probably better if we say nothing about it in the meeting tomorrow.

REVEREND WRIGHT I disagree. We should perhaps seek the counsel of fellow clergymen concerning this supernatural event. Listen, the drumming grows fainter. It has stopped.

NARRATOR On the following night the two ministers were again awakened in the middle of the night.

GHOST DRUMMER Thump, thump, thump, thump, thump,
Thump, thump, thump, thump, thump.

REVEREND LOW Matthew, I have been seized violently by the great toe. Whatever it is, it won't let go!

REVEREND WRIGHT Listen to the drums. They are playing the 'Scots Traveler.' The drums grow louder and I feel, I feel . . .

REVEREND LOW You feel the same as I, a weight greater than a human form.

NARRATOR Suddenly a candle shed light throughout the room. Holding the candle was a fellow minister. He stood looking at the two frightened clergymen and laughed at their fears.

REVEREND TRUE Fear not, my brothers. The drum is a washpan borrowed from Mistress True. It was a human hand, Sir, that secured your toe and a sack of potatoes that weighted you down. I believe it was the wine you imbibed last night that brought the pounding to your head.

NARRATOR The story of the two clergymen and their encounter with the ghostly drummer appeared in a letter published in the *Pennsylvania Gazette* in April of 1730. The letter told of the foolishness of the two in believing in ghosts and how the ghostly drummer had been put to rest by a fellow clergyman.

(The scene now shifts to the Wright home just after the publication of the letter.)

MRS. WRIGHT Charles, I don't know how I am going to cope with your foolishness. Ghostly drummer indeed! Why, I can hardly pass a member of the congregation without hearing snickers . . . that's right, snickers!

REVEREND WRIGHT My dear, it is true that the drummer on the second night was a hoax perpetrated by a fellow minister. But the first night I assure you, was no hoax. See, here is another letter from a writer in *The Gazette* who agrees.

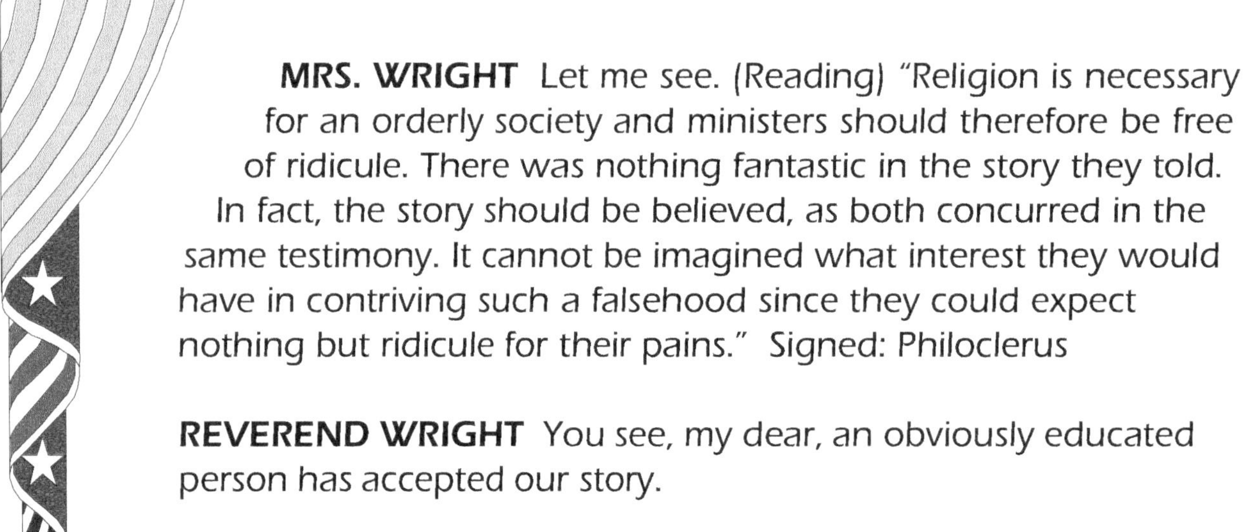

MRS. WRIGHT Let me see. (Reading) "Religion is necessary for an orderly society and ministers should therefore be free of ridicule. There was nothing fantastic in the story they told. In fact, the story should be believed, as both concurred in the same testimony. It cannot be imagined what interest they would have in contriving such a falsehood since they could expect nothing but ridicule for their pains." Signed: Philoclerus

REVEREND WRIGHT You see, my dear, an obviously educated person has accepted our story.

MRS. WRIGHT Acceptance or not, the next call to a meeting in Philadelphia you will refuse. Fortunately there are no ghosts in our parish.

SUPER RESEARCH CHALLENGE

WRITER THREE The author of the story about the two clergymen and of the letter defending them was the publisher of the *Pennsylvania Gazette* who in 1730 was well known for publishing stories which were hoaxes. His name was____

Among other hoaxes he perpetrated on an unsuspecting public were____

____

____

____

____

____

THE GHOSTLY DRUMMER OF TEDWORTH

ADDITIONAL READING

Benjamin Franklin by P. Joseph. Abdo, 1996.
The life of Franklin with emphasis on his inventions.

Benjamin Franklin by T. Usel. Capstone, 1996.
Full color photographs highlight the life of Franklin.

Benjamin Franklin, Founding Father and Inventor by L. Foster. Enslow, 1997.
Biography of the American inventor and statesman.

Dangerous Ghosts by Daniel Cohen. Putnam, 1996.
Accounts of ghosts that bring danger to those they visit.

Ghost in the House by Daniel Cohen. Scholastic, 1993.
Stories of some of the best known haunted houses in the world.

Ghostly Warnings by Daniel Cohen. Putnam, 1994.
Warnings received by humans believed to have come from ghosts.

Ghosts of War by Daniel Cohen. Putnam, 1989.
Reported sightings of ghosts from many different wars.

Great Ghosts by Daniel Cohen. Putnam, 1993.
Stories of some of the most famous ghosts in history.

Ghosts and Poltergeists by G. Meier. Capstone, 1991.
Examines evidence supporting the existence of ghosts.

1730 THE GHOSTLY DRUMMER OF TEDWORTH

Aldridge, Alfred. "**Franklin and the Ghostly Drummer of Tedworth**." *William and Mary Quarterly*, Third Series, Volume 7, Issue 4 (Oct. 1950). pp. 559-567

Blackman, W. Haden. **Field Guide to North American Hauntings**. Three Rivers Press, 1998.

Rule, Leslie. Coast to Coast Ghosts. McMeel Pub., 2001.

1775 THE GHOST OF THE BOSTON MASSACRE

While the ghost may be a hoax, historical details in this play are true. However, the Paul Revere engraving which inflamed anti-British sentiment in the colonies contained several untruths! Young researchers are challenged to find them.

Reading Parts Peter, Marty, Madge

PETER My name is Peter Parsons, better known as "Peeks", I guess because I'm always peeking into things that are none of my business. That's how it all happened. It was one of those boring afternoons with nothing to do when Marty and I decided to explore the old Simpson place.

MARTY Are you sure we should go in there, Peeks? Looks like its ready to fall down.

PETER What do you expect for a place that's over 200 years old?

WRITER ONE Describe this broken-down 200 year-old Colonial house. Research a typical home that existed in Boston in the 1770s. Include as many details in your description as possible. What parts of the house might be missing that were once there?

____

____

____

____

MARTY Wait, what's that? There's a strange light in the window. Peeks, you're not going any closer are you?

PETER I can't explain. Something's been pulling me toward this house all day. Look, what's that on the porch? It looks like . . . it can't be . . . it is . . . a ghost!

MADGE Welcome. I have been waiting for you for over 200 years. Such a long, long time to wait . . . but I knew that one day you would come.

MARTY I don't believe we're seeing this.

WRITER TWO Describe the girl. How tall is she? What color is her hair? What would one remember most about her appearance? How would a young woman be dressed in the 1770s? What material would the dress be made from?

____

____

____

PETER Are you sure it's us you are looking for, Mam?

MADGE Oh, yes. Only through you can I finally rest in peace. I know you can find it and tell all the world that I was not a traitor. The Patriots thought I was the one who told the Redcoats that the engraving was in the tavern. But I would never do a thing like that. I did my best to save it, but I died before the engraving could be found by the Patriots.

PETER What engraving?

MADGE Why Mr. Revere's engraving, of course. You see, this house used to be a Boston Tavern where I was a barmaid. Sam Adams, John Hancock and Paul Revere met here often. They were determined to get the Redcoats out of Boston, and when the massacre happened they knew they had to act!

MARTY There was a massacre in Boston?

MADGE Yes. The people were up in arms about the high taxes and the British ships of war in Boston Harbor. When the Redcoats landed on Long Wharf they were quartered in the Old State House. And they paraded about like they owned all of Boston. When tempers got too high, that's when the massacre happened.

WRITER THREE Describe the Boston Massacre. Use descriptive words. How many were killed? Who fired first? Where did it take place?

____

____

____

MADGE After the massacre, Mr. Adams decided that every colony should know of the tyranny of the British, so Mr. Revere made a copper engraving of the scene so that copies could be sent to all the colonies. I was sent to Mr. Revere's silversmith shop to get the engraving to show to Mr. Adams for approval. I had just returned to the tavern kitchen when the Redcoats burst in. I barely had time to hide the engraving before I met my death.

WRITER FOUR Describe the raiding of the tavern by the Redcoats. Research what their weapons looked like. Tell how the people in the tavern might have reacted.

____

____

____

____

PETER You mean the engraving is still here?

MADGE It must be. I ran up the attic stairs ahead of the Redcoats and hid it in a trunk. But unfortunately, on the way down I tripped and fell to my death. If you can find it and tell the people my story, then I can rest in peace. Follow me now to the attic.

PETER Come on, Marty, let's find it. Just a few more stairs to climb. Look! There's the trunk. Hold the lid up so I can reach inside. I can feel something smooth with my hand. I'll just get a good grip on it . . . GOT IT . . . WOW . . . look at this!

WRITER FIVE Describe the Paul Revere engraving. Many encyclopedias and internet sites have pictures of it. You may be able to print out a full color copy from the Internet.

____

____

____

MARTY Now that we have the engraving, what are we supposed to do with it?

MADGE You must have it displayed so that all Americans will know that I did not destroy it . . . or worse yet, that I did not give it to the Redcoats. Only then can I rest in peace. And you will receive a reward . . .

WRITER SIX Tell how Marty and Peter will carry out Madge's wish.

____

____

____

PETER Getting national attention wasn't easy to do but we did it. Madge can rest in peace now.

MARTY She did say something about a reward . . . maybe we should go by the old Simpson place today.

PETER There it is! In that box on the porch. Let's get it open – quick!

PETER AND MARTY Of all the things it could possibly be, we *never* expected this!

WRITER SEVEN Describe the reward. It needs to be something from the Colonial period that Madge would have to give.

____

____

____

____

PETER Hey, Marty, tomorrow why don't we explore the old Townsend house . . . who knows what . . .or who . . . we'll find there!

SUPER RESEARCH CHALLENGE

WRITER EIGHT On March 5, 1770, a mob of men and boys taunted a British sentry who was guarding the custom house. British soldiers arrived and fired wildly into the crowd, killing five men and wounding six others. Paul Revere's engraving of the Boston Massacre stirred anti-British sentiment among the colonists but four details in the color prints made from the engraving are not accurate. Discover what these inaccuracies are.

THE GHOST OF THE BOSTON MASSACRE

ADDTIONAL READING

And Then What Happened, Paul Revere? by Jean Fritz. Coward, 1973.
An account of the life of Paul Revere including his famous ride.

Boston by D. Kent. Children's Press, 1998.
A guide to the history and landmarks of this famous city.

The Boston Coffee Party by Doreen Rappaport. HarperCollins, 1988.
Two sisters help a group of Boston women get coffee from a greedy merchant.

Boston Tea Party by M. Burgan. Children's Press, 1992.
An in-depth look at the events that shaped our nation.

Boston Tea Party by Libby O'Neill. Millbrook Press, 1996.
The events that led to the Boston Tea Party and the early stages of the American Revolution.

Boston Tea Party by Stephen Kroll. Holiday House, 1998.
The historical background of the Boston Tea Party when the Americans revolted against the British.

Boston Tea Party: Rebellion in the Colonies by J. Knight. Enslow, 1999.
The events in Boston in 1773 as the colonists protested against British taxes.

Mr. Revere and Me by Robert Lawson. Little Brown, 1953.
A humorous account of Paul Revere's ride as told by his horse.

Paul Revere by M. Lee. Watts, 1987.
His life from childhood to young adulthood.

Story of the Boston Massacre by Mary Kay Phelan. Crowell, 1976.
Gives the underlying causes and description of the event.

The Tavern at the Ferry by Edwin Tunis. Crowell, 1973.
An account of dramatic events that happened at this scene during the Revolutionary War.

1775 THE BOSTON MASSACRE

Boston Gazette and Country Journal, March 6, 1770. p.1

Dickson, Alice. **Boston Massacre**. Franklin Watts, 1968.

Zobel, Hiller. **The Boston Massacre**. Norton, 1996.

1776 THE LIBERTY BELL

The Liberty Bell rang on July 8, 1776, to summon the citizens of Philadelphia to the first public reading of the Declaration of Independence. In 1996 the bell was once again a cause for rebellion throughout the land. Read on to find out why.

Reading Parts Narrator, Carlos, Louise, Jenny, Mrs. Evans

NARRATOR The scene is a sixth grade classroom. The date is April 1, 1996.

LOUISE It is a disgrace! We ought to write the President.

CARLOS Well, somebody should do something. That bell belongs to all the people. How could it be sold? It's a national treasure, even if it did get a crack in it when it was rung in 1776.

JENNY Maybe it was sold by an Act of Congress. Lots of things happen that way. And Carlos, the crack didn't happen in 1776.

WRITER ONE Tell when the bell was first hung in Independence Hall steeple. What happened to it the first time it was rung?

____

____

____

JENNY Didn't they ever try to fix the crack?

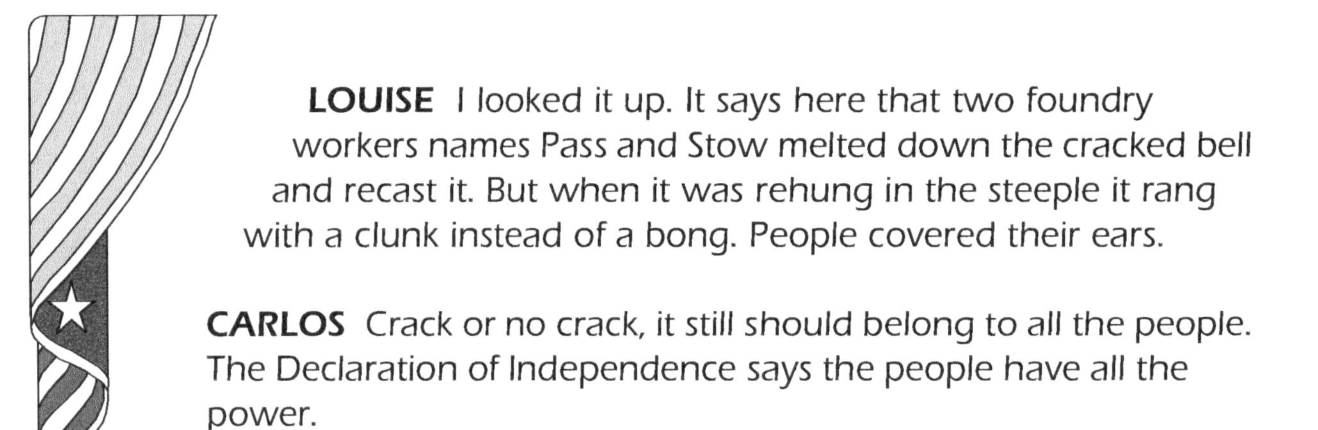

LOUISE I looked it up. It says here that two foundry workers names Pass and Stow melted down the cracked bell and recast it. But when it was rehung in the steeple it rang with a clunk instead of a bong. People covered their ears.

CARLOS Crack or no crack, it still should belong to all the people. The Declaration of Independence says the people have all the power.

WRITER TWO What is The Declaration of Independence? Who was the man who read it aloud for the first time on July 8, 1776?

____

____

____

LOUISE That's right. And a year later when the British entered Philadelphia it was taken down and hidden so they wouldn't melt it down and use it for cannon.

JENNY Wow, I don't see how they could hide something that big.

WRITER THREE How much did the Liberty Bell weigh when it was cast?

____

____

____

LOUISE They hid it in the floorboards in a church in Allentown. That kept the British from getting their hands on it.

CARLOS But somebody else has their hands on it now, and it's not right that one company should own it!

MRS. EVANS What are you children talking about?

LOUISE See, it's right here in the *New York Times*. (Reading from the paper) April 1, 1996. Taco Bell® Buys the Liberty Bell. "In an effort to help the national debt, Taco Bell® is pleased to announce that we have agreed to purchase the Liberty Bell, one of our country's most historic treasures. It will now be called the 'Taco Liberty Bell' and will still be accessible to the American public for viewing. While some may find this controversial, we hope our move will prompt other corporations to take similar action to do their part to reduce the country's debt."

JENNY If it's in the paper it must be true.

MRS. EVANS It is true that newspapers try to be accurate in their stories. What you have overlooked is the most important part of the paper.

NARRATOR What did the students miss? Do you know?

SUPER RESEARCH CHALLENGE

WRITER FOUR Find out more about the Taco Liberty Bell. How would anyone reading the full page ad by Taco Bell® know that it was a hoax? Did the hoax increase Taco Bell's® sales?

____

____

____

____

____

THE LIBERTY BELL

ADDITIONAL READING

American Army of Two by J. Greeson. Lerner, 1991.
Sisters divert a British attack by playing a fife and drum to imitate the approach of American troops.

The American Revolution by Bruce Bliven. Random House, 1958.
The causes, battles and results of the Revolution.

American Revolution: War for Independence by A. Carter. Watts, 1993.
Discusses the causes and aftermath of the Revolution.

The American Revolutionaries: A History in Their Own Words by Milton Meltzer. Crowell, 1987.
Accounts of the Revolution told through diaries, letters and other documents.

Ben and Me by Robert Lawson. Little Brown, 1939.
A young mouse takes credit for the inventions of Benjamin Franklin.

Colonial Living by Edwin Tunis. Crowell, 1976.
Everyday aspects of Colonial life.

Founding Mothers: Women of America in the Revolutionary Era by L. Depauw. Houghton-Mifflin, 1975.
Daily lives and contributions of women living during the Revolutionary period.

The Fourth of July Story by Alice Dalgliesh. Scribner, 1956.
The writing of the Declaration of Independence, its reception by the people and the Colonies.

Liberty Bell by G. Sakurai. Children's Press, 1996.
History of the famous bell.

Liberty Bell: The Sounds of Freedom by J. Wilson. Child's World, 1999.
The history of the bell and how it came to symbolize freedom.

Story of the Thirteen Colonies by Clifford Alderman. Random House, 1966.
Events leading to the establishment of the Colonies.

1776 THE LIBERTY BELL

Frank, Robert. "**Taco Bell's Gag Over the Liberty Bell Doesn't Leave Philly Cracking Up**" *Wall Street Journal*, April 2, 1996.

Johnson, Greg. "**Taco Bell's Ad Was a Burrito Short of a Combination Plate**" *Los Angeles Times*, April 2, 1996.

1817 THE GLOUCESTER SEA SERPENT

In the 19th Century over 190 sightings, many by reliable witnesses, were made of a strange sea creature off the coast of Gloucester, Massachusetts. In the 20th century only 56 sightings were recorded. Does the creature actually exist or are the sightings a way to get tourists to the City of Gloucester?

Reading Parts Narrator, Mrs. Story, Amos Story, Solomon Allen, Matthew Gaffney, Cheever Felch, John Brown

NARRATOR What is 100 feet long, has a head like a horse, a body as round as a large barrel and swims in the sea? The people of Gloucester, Massachusetts, can tell you. Gloucester is not only an ideal port for cargo ships, but an ideal place for a sea serpent to live.

WRITER ONE Research Gloucester, Massachusetts. Where is it located? Why was it an ideal port for cargo ships in the 1800s? Why would people of that time claim that it was an ideal place for a sea serpent to live?

____

____

____

MRS STORY I am Mrs. Amos Story. My husband and I saw the creature on August 10, 1817. At first I thought it was a tree trunk washed up on the rocks of Ten Pound Island. But as I watched through the telescope it moved, and when I looked again, it was gone.

AMOS STORY My name is Amos Story. It was between twelve and one o'clock on August 10th, 1817, when I first saw the creature. His head was shaped like a sea turtle but larger than the head of a dog. I could not see more than 10 or 12 feet of his body but he moved rapidly through the water, I should say, a mile or two in three minutes.

SOLOMON ALLEN I am Shipmaster Solomon Allen III, and on August 12, 1817, I saw the Gloucester Sea Serpent. His head was formed something like the head of a rattlesnake. When he moved on the surface of the water, his motion was slow, sometimes playing in circles. Two days later, my shipmate, Matthew Gaffney saw it and shot at it.

MATTHEW GAFFNEY I did not know whether to believe Solomon's story or not. He is not a drinking man, and he is an experienced sailor. But a sea serpent? I thought not, until two days later I saw it. I had a good gun and took aim and shot at his head, and I think I must have hit him. He turned toward us immediately after I had fired, and I thought he was coming at us, but he sank down and went directly under our boat. You have to know the size of a typical sailing ship to see how lucky we were not to be overturned.

WRITER TWO Research sailing ships of the early 1800s. How many tons did a typical sailing ship weigh? How long was it? How many sails? How many men in a typical crew?

____

____

____

NARRATOR Eighteen different sightings of the sea serpent were reported in 1817. Most of the descriptions were very similar, and many from reliable witnesses like Cheever Felch, aboard a United States schooner.

CHEEVER FELCH The creature I saw had a head about three feet in circumference and its length was close to 100 feet. I speak with a degree of certainty being much accustomed to measuring distances. His motion was like that of a fresh water snake. I have been much acquainted with snakes in our interior waters. His motion was the same.

NARRATOR Another report of an 1817 sighting comes from John Brown, an experienced sailor who at first thought he was viewing a shipwreck.

JOHN BROWN That is true. I saw three to four miles in the distance something that looked like a ship's mast, rising and falling. I could see, also, timbers sticking up. But as we approached nearer, I found that what had looked like timbers to be a number of porpoises and black fish playing and jumping around a large Sea-Serpent which I had supposed to be the mast.

NARRATOR Could a sea serpent really exist today? There were 190 sightings off the coast of Gloucester in the 1900s. Only 56 sightings were reported in the 1900s and most of those in the first half of the century. The last sighting off the coast of Massachusetts was in 1962. Some people believe that this is a Mosasaur that has survived from the Cretaceous period.

WRITER THREE Find descriptions of the Mosasaur. Compare the descriptions with those given by witnesses of the Gloucester Sea Serpent. Do you agree or disagree with the theory?

___

___

___

NARRATOR Another theory is that an elephant seal might look like a sea monster to one not familiar with elephant seals. Or possibly the creature was a giant anaconda that had fallen off a ship coming from South America.

WRITER FOUR Research elephant seals and anacondas. Describe their appearance. How large can each grow? Compare your descriptions the with witnesses' descriptions of the sea serpent. Is this a good theory or not? Why?

____

____

____

NARRATOR In 1997, after 30 years of no sightings, a report was made of a strange creature sighted off the coast of Fortune Bay, Newfoundland. It was said to have a six-foot-long neck with a head like a horse and dark eyes on the front of its face. Some experts theorize that over-fishing of the waters of the Massachusetts' coast caused the creature to look elsewhere for food. Work is going on now to revitalize the fish population. If the fish return, will the Sea Serpent return with them? What do you think?

<u>**SUPER RESEARCH CHALLENGE**</u>

WRITER FIVE Why were there many more sightings of the Sea Serpent in the 1800s than there are today?

____

____

____

____

____

____

THE GLOUCESTER SEA SERPENT

ADDITIONAL READING

Monster at Loch Ness by S. Berke. Raintree, 1983.
The legends and evidence concerning the existence of the Loch Nes monster.

Monsters and Magic: Myths of North and South America by S. Ross. Milbrook, 1998.
Collection of myths and legends.

Monsters and Other Creatures by C. Taylor. Tundra Books, 1995.
Legends from tribes across North America.

Monsters of the Deep by S. Pirotta. Raintree, 1996.
Explore the underwater world and learn about sharks, whales, mysterious sea serpents and more.

Monsters of the Deep by S. Ross. Lerner, 1998.
A dive into the dangerous waters of the world to discover the dangerous creatures that live there.

The Sea by R. Kerrod. Capstone, 1999.
Learn about tides, curents and animal life.

Sea Animals by Dorling Kindersley editors. Dorling Kindersley, 1992.
Color photographs and descriptions of animals that live in the sea.

Sea Creatures with Many Arms by D. Souza. Lerner, 1998.
A look at different sea creatures with multiple arms.

Sea Snakes by D. Souza. Lerner, 1998.
The life cycle and behavior of sea snakes.

Sea Snakes by H. Seward. Rourke, 1998.
A look at sea snakes and their gentle behavior despite their scary appearance.

Serpent by Clive Cussler. Pocket Books, 2000.
An underwater exploration team works overtime to save the world.

1817 THE GLOUCESTER SEA SERPENT

O'Neill, J.P. **The Great New England Sea Serpent**. Down East Books, 1999.
Spaeth, Frank. **Mysteries and Monsters of the Sea**. Random House, 2001.

In 1824, a respected and educated orator named Lozier offered jobs to the unemployed to save Manhattan, part of which he claimed was sinking due to too many buildings at its tip. Was this gainful employment or a hoax?

Reading Parts Narrator, Jenny, Jacob, Orator, Lozier, Butcher, Tradesman

JACOB Boy, it's hot. This is the hottest summer I can remember.

JENNY I slept out on the fire escape last night. It was the only place there was a breeze. What do you want to do now?

JACOB We could walk over to Castle Clinton. It's open to the public now. I've always wanted to see inside a real fort.

WRITER ONE Research Castle Clinton. Why was it built? Where is it located? Does it exist today?

____

____

____

JENNY We could go down to Centre Market and listen to the speeches. Maybe Lozier will be there today.

NARRATOR The children made their way to Centre Market at Mulberry and Spring Streets to join the butchers and the tradesmen listening to a soapbox orator.

ORATOR Yes, gentlemen, our president is right in keeping foreign settlements off our soil. America should be for Americans!

WRITER TWO Who was president in 1824? What famous Doctrine is he noted for?

____

____

____

BUTCHER Enough of boring speeches! Where is Lozier? We haven't heard from him in weeks.

TRADESMAN He's in that corner over there. I tried to speak to him but he asked me to leave him alone.

BUTCHER It's time we found out what's wrong. Come with me.

NARRATOR The delegation approached their favorite speaker with concern and asked why he was no longer taking the speaker's platform.

LOZIER Gentlemen, I have been pondering a great problem, one that will affect everyone's life. The problem is right here in the Battery.

WRITER THREE Describe the Battery section of Manhattan in 1824. What could be found there?

____

____

____

LOZIER Have you stopped to think about the consequences of all of the heavy construction that has gone on in the Battery in recent years? The weight of all this construction is causing the island to tip. Look down the hill and see for yourselves.

NARRATOR Lozier took the crowd to the center of the street and told them to look down the road. From City Hall to the opposite end was all downhill.

JACOB He's right. The land is lower by the water than it is here at the Market.

JENNY This sounds serious. What do you think might happen?

JACOB Shhh. Let's listen.

LOZIER The seriousness of the problem cannot be under estimated. The weight of all of these buildings on the Battery end is causing it to tip. The inevitable result will be that this end of the Island will eventually break off into the sea!

NARRATOR At that moment there was sheer panic among the listeners. There were cries of how soon? It can't be! You can see he's right! What can we do?

LOZIER Now is not the time for panic but for action. Give me a few more days and I believe I will have a solution to the problem.

NARRATOR Several days later Lozier was again ready to speak. The concerned crowd numbered in the hundreds as the people waited breathlessly for Lozier's solution.

LOZIER Beginning at the Northern end we must saw off the island and tow it past Ellis Island out to sea.

WRITER FOUR Describe Ellis Island in 1824. What, if anything was it used for?

____

____

____

____

____

____

LOZIER Once out to sea we will turn Manhattan around and reattach it.

JENNY That makes sense. Then the heavier buildings will be attached to the mainland with few buildings on the Battery end.

JACOB They will need laws to keep more buildings from being built in the Battery so it doesn't happen again.

LOZIER At least 500 men will be needed for the job. If you are willing to work, I will put your names in this ledger now.

BUTCHER I'd like to help, but I can't leave my butcher shop.

LOZIER Never fear, Sir, your services will be greatly needed. Not only will we need carpenters to construct a barracks to house the workers but also a separate building to house a mess hall. All butchers should submit their bids for 500 heads of cattle and 3000 chickens.

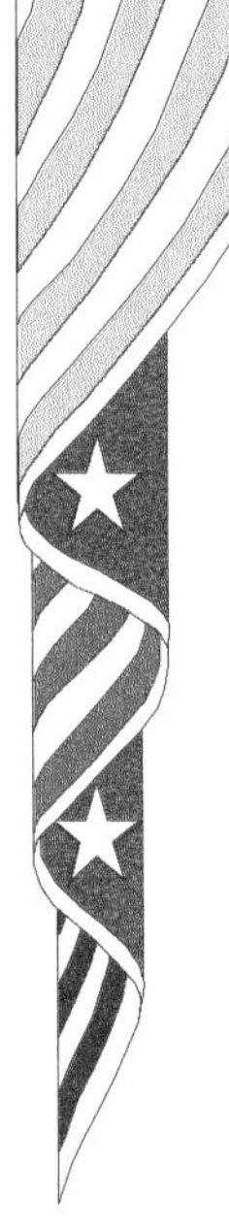

JENNY Both of our dads are carpenters. We should tell them about the work.

LOZIER There will be work for everyone. Blacksmiths should submit bids for 15 saws 100 feet in length and three feet in height. We'll need miles of heavy chains to wrap around trees and attach to the 1500 boats that are being built.

JACOB My uncle is a blacksmith. He'll want to help.

LOZIER We will also need pitmen to work the saws under water. It is a dangerous job and only for those with great lung capacity. But it will pay more than the other jobs. Line up to see if you qualify.

NARRATOR A long line of men formed. Lozier timed how long each one could hold his breath.

JACOB I can hold my breath a long time.

JENNY Maybe so, but you're not strong enough to hold a 100-foot saw.

NARRATOR Days passed and nothing happened. The people began to ask about a starting date. The date was announced when all were to show up on the Battery end for a parade to City Hall. It would be a parade not soon forgotten.

WRITER FIVE What is the most famous annual parade that New Yorkers look forward to? When is it held?

____

____

____

NARRATOR When the day arrived a large crowd of men showed up ready to begin work. A band was there to lead the parade The one man who was missing was Lozier. Can you guess why?

SUPER RESEARCH CHALLENGE

WRITER SIX Describe Battery Park as it exists today.

____

____

____

____

____

____

____

____

____

____

MANHATTAN WORKERS NEEDED?

ADDTIONAL READING

City in the Clouds by T. Abbott. Scholastic, 1999.
Fantasy about a kingdom that is threatened with extinction.

City of Gold by P. Berton. Simon & Schuster, 1967.
Stories of greed, courage and foolhardiness.

Ellis Island by R. Stein. Children's Press, 1992.
The history, closing and restoration of Ellis Island.

Ellis Island, Doorway to Freedom by Stephen Kroll. Holiday House, 1995.
Facts, dates and numbers are included in this history of the island.

New York by V. Schomp. Morning Glory Press, 1997.
Explore the unique character of New York through its land , cultural diversity and stories of success.

New York by A. Gelman. Lerner, 1992.
Introduces the geography, history and people of New York.

New York by C. Hat. Creative Education, 2000.
Captures the character of New York City by exploring the past and investigating what the future may hold.

New York by D. Fradin. Children's Press, 1993.
Quick reference on the history, geography and population of New York.

New York City by D. Kent. Children's Press, 1996.
The history and people of New York City with color photographs.

Parade by Donald Crews. Econo-Clad Books. 1999.
Various elements of a parade including street vendors, spectators, marchers, bands and floats.

1824 MANHATTAN WORKERS NEEDED?

DeVoe, Thomas F. **The Market Book**. Franklin Publishing, 1862. pp. 462-64

Feinstein, Sanna. **Naming New York: Manhattan Places and How They Got Their Names**. New York University Press, 2001.

Sante, Luc. **Lures and Snares of Old New York**. Vintage Books, 1992.

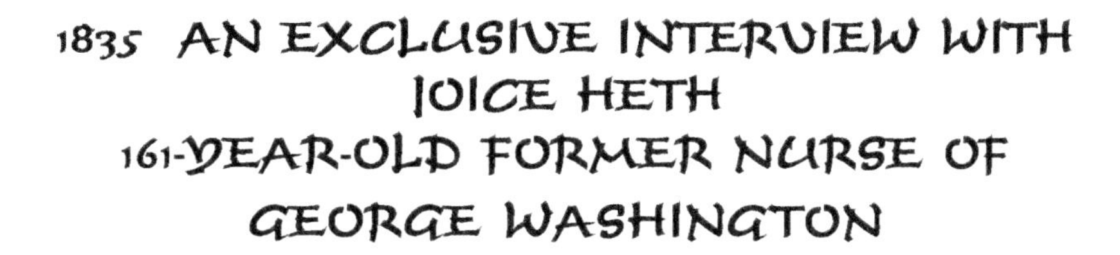

Joice Heth was an elderly black woman whom a young P.T. Barnum put on display in 1835, advertising that she was the 161-year-old fomer nurse of George Washington. Heth entertained audiences with tales about young George, and her exhibition drew considerable attention.

Reading Parts Narrator, P.T. Barnum, Reporter, Joice Heth

NARRATOR The year is 1835. The setting is Niblo's Garden in New York City where the exhibitions of P.T. Barnum, the world's greatest showman, can be visited and viewed.

P.T. BARNUM Step right up, step right up, ladies and gentlemen. This is your one and only and possibly last opportunity to see the world's oldest living human being. Yes, indeed, Joice Heth's amazing age has been documented to be 161 years of age. Not only that, ladies and gentlemen, she is the former nurse of George Washington, the first President of the United States.

WRITER ONE Who was P.T. Barnum? Why was he called the "World's Greatest Showman?" What were some of the amazing Barnum spectaculars that people paid to see?

____

____

____

REPORTER Mr. Barnum, my paper, *The New York Sun,* has sent me to interview Joice Heth to determine the truth of your statements about her. Do you have any objection to such an interview?

P.T. BARNUM Not at all, son, not at all. She may weigh only 46 pounds but she is alert and cheerful, speaks freely, sings hymns and can relate many anecdotes about little Georgy as she calls him. There is no doubt about her age. She has legal documents to prove it. In addition, the most learned and scientific men in the country have visited her, and after conversing with and examining her, declare her to be the greatest curiosity in the world.

REPORTER Could I meet her now?

P.T. BARNUM Step this way. Miz Heth, this young fellow is a reporter from *The New York Sun.* He'd like to chat with you for a bit.

REPORTER (Speaking loudly) I'm most pleased to make your acquaintance Miz Heth.

JOICE HETH No need to shout, young man. I may be blind but my hearing is as good as it was back when old Augustine shouted for me to find Georgy and get him cleaned up for company.

REPORTER Old Augustine?

JOICE HETH Augustine Washington, Georgy's daddy.

REPORTER When you talk about little Georgy do you mean George Washington, the first President of the United States?

JOICE HETH Who else would I be talking about? I was 58 years old when little Georgy was born, but I remember it like yesterday.

REPORTER If you were 58 years old in 1731, when George Washington was born, that means YOU were born in 1674.

JOICE HETH That's right, sonny. I first saw the light of day on the Island of Madagascar in 1674 just like Mr. Barnum's sign outside says. It was as good a place as any to grow up, that is until the slavers came.

WRITER TWO Find information about the Island of Madagascar. Where is it located? During what years were the people of Madagascar captured and sold to slave traders?

___

___

___

REPORTER How did you get to this country?

JOICE HETH At the age of 15 I was cruelly torn from my parents' home by one of those inhuman beings who, in those days, to enrich themselves, sold human flesh. I was brought to America on a slave ship, sold to Thomas Buckner, a Virginia planter, who several years later sold me to the Washington family. When little Georgy was born, I became his nurse.

REPORTER Since you were more than a half century old at that time, why were you given his care? I would think George's mother would have wanted a younger nurse for him.

JOICE HETH Because I faithfully discharged all of my duties in the household, I had the full confidence of all the family. They treated me more as a hired servant than a slave. I was entrusted with the whole care and management of both the kitchen and nursery.

REPORTER Even so, at age 58 looking after a lively young boy could not have been easy.

JOICE HETH Slaves don't have choices. You do what you are told. And yes, little Georgy was a handful!

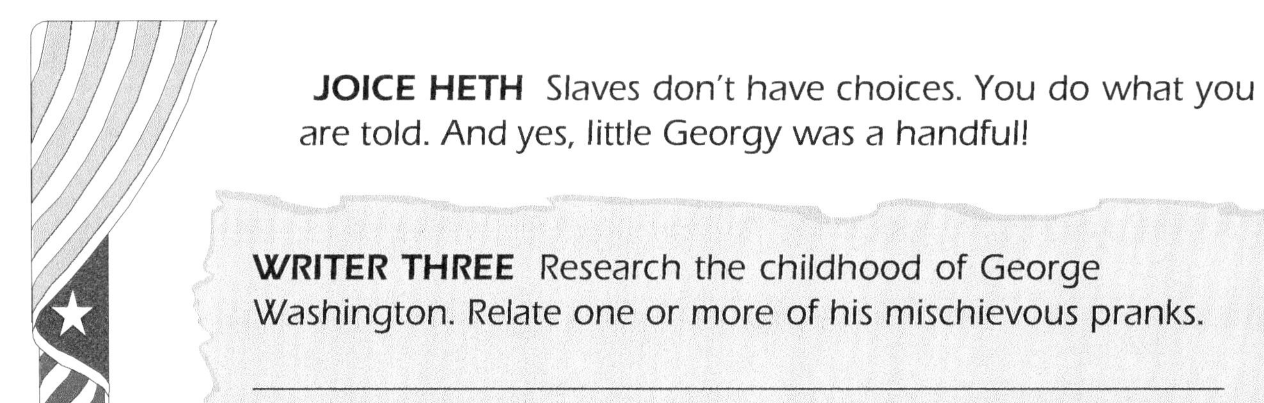

WRITER THREE Research the childhood of George Washington. Relate one or more of his mischievous pranks.

____

____

____

REPORTER Were you ever married?

JOICE HETH In 1694, at the age of 20, I was married to a slave named Peter who belonged to a neighbor of the Washington family. We had 15 children. All dead now.

REPORTER I'm sorry to hear that. Were you able to attend the inauguration when George Washington became the first President of the United States?

JOICE HETH If you can do your sums you should know that I was 115 years old at the time. Traveling wasn't easy even for young folks, so I didn't make the trip to New York. But my goodness, it must have been some ceremony. The family told me about it later.

WRITER FOUR Research the inauguration of George Washington. Write an account of the ceremony as family members might have related it to Joice.

____

____

____

REPORTER Mr. Barnum says you have documents to prove your age. Could I see them?

JOICE Here , Since I can't see, I like to hear them read aloud, but you give them right back. I value them highly.

REPORTER (Reading from one of the certificates) "This shall certify that I, the subscriber, Thomas Merton, was born in the town of Paris in the State of Kentucky. My age is 71 years on the 17th of February, 1835. I have ever known Joice Heth, the old colored woman. When I first remember Aunt Joice, as we called her, she was totally blind and unable to work, which must have been 55 years ago. It was always understood that Joice was the nurse of George Washington, and slave of his father. She is very religious and honest, and I believe the most implicit confidence can be put in her word, for nothing in my opinion would tempt her to utter a falsehood."

JOICE And there's three more just like that one.

REPORTER Do you enjoy being on display now and having people come to look at you and ask questions?

JOICE The money Mr. Barnum pays me will purchase the freedom of two of my five great-grandchildren who are now in bondage in Kentucky. What else would I need money for? My needs are few, tea, cornbread, my pipe, a little tobacco and dog food which I munch now and then.

REPORTER Dog food?

JOICE HETH The doctors say I shouldn't have it, but what do they know? If I had listened to them I'd have been dead years ago. I've never in my life taken any medicine and never will.

P.T. BARNUM Well, son, I hope you will now attest in your paper as to the veracity of our claims about Miz Heth. She needs to get ready for this afternoon's exhibition.

REPORTER (To the audience) Veracity? You can read my interview with Miz Heth in tomorrow's *Sun Times*. I'll draw no conclusions. You'll have to decide for yourselves . . . is Joice Heth really who she claims to be, or is it a hoax?

SUPER RESEARCH CHALLENGE

WRITER FIVE Research P.T. Barnum and Joice Heth. Report on how her 161-year-old age was proved to be a hoax.

JOICE HETH: 161-YEAR-OLD FORMER NURSE OF GEORGE WASHINGTON

ADDITIONAL READING

George Washington by T. Bruns. Chelsea House, 1987.
Biography about the first U.S. president.

George Washington by Ingri D'Aulaire. Doubledday, 1996.
Tells of the major events in his life and the upbringing that endowed him with leadership qualities.

George Washington by Z. Kent. Children's Press, 1986.
Traces the life and accomplishments of the first president.

George Washington by T. Usel. Capstone, 1996.
Full color photographs accompany this short biography.

George Washington by A. Welsbacher. Abdo, 1997.
Biography of the first president.

George Washington, The Man Who Would Not Be King by Stephen Krensky. Scholastic, 1991.
Well-written account of the life and work of Washington.

George Washington: Young Leader by Augusta Stevenson. Bobbs-Merrill, 1959.
Recounts the childhood of America's first president.

George Washington's Breakfast by Jean Fritz. Putnam, 1998.
A namesake of George Washington wants to find out what he had for breakfast.

George Washington's Mother by Jean Fritz. Putnam, 1992.
Humorously depicts Washington's mother as a manipulative and stubborn worrywort.

George Washington's Socks by Elvira Woodruff. Scholastic, 1992.
Modern day children ae transported back to the time of Washington.

P.T. Barnum by D. Wright. Raintree, 1997.
Biography of the outrageous promoter who created the greatest show on earth.

1835 JOICE HETH

Reiss, Benjamin. "**P.T. Barnum, Joice Heth and Antebellum Spectacles of Race**," *American Quarterly*, Vol. 51, No.1 (March 1999).

Adams, Bluford. **E. Pluribus Barnum: The Great Showman & the Making of U.S. Popular Culture**, University of Minnesota Press, 1997.

1842 THE FEEJEE MERMAID

Today one of the most asked about specimens in the Peabody Museum of Archaeology and Ethnology is a 16-nch mermaid. The Museum is located at Harvard University. Is the mermaid real or is it a hoax?

Reading Parts Martha, Grandfather, Grandmother

MARTHA (Reading aloud) "The little mermaid lifted her glorified eyes towards the sun, and felt them, for the first time, filling with tears. On the ship, in which she had left the prince, there were life and noise; she saw him and his beautiful bride searching for her; sorrowfully they gazed at the pearly foam, as if they knew she had thrown herself into the waves." Oh, grandfather, "The Little Mermaid" is such a sad story. Why do you suppose Hans Christian Andersen didn't write happy endings?

WRITER ONE Tell about the childhood of Hans Christian Andersen.

GRANDFATHER People who aren't happy themselves have a hard time seeing happy endings for others.

MARTHA At least it is just a story. Everyone knows that mermaids don't really exist.

GRANDFATHER Don't be too sure. Lots of folks have seen mermaids.

MARTHA Like who?

GRANDFATHER Christopher Columbus wrote in his ship's log that he saw three mermaids in the ocean off Haiti in January of 1493. They came quite high out of the water and were not as pretty as he expected because he said their faces looked like men.

WRITER TWO Where is Haiti? Which of Columbus's voyages took him there in 1493? What did he find when he got there?

____

____

____

____

____

MARTHA More than likely Columbus saw a manatee. They have pretty ugly faces.

GRANDMOTHER What has ugly faces?

MARTHA The mermaids that Columbus said he saw. But they weren't really mermaids.

GRANDMOTHER Why not? If my great-grandmother could see one, I guess Columbus could.

MARTHA Your great-grandmother saw a real mermaid?

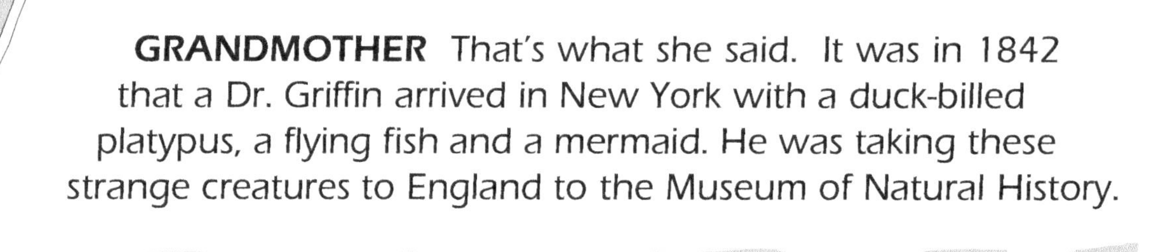

GRANDMOTHER That's what she said. It was in 1842 that a Dr. Griffin arrived in New York with a duck-billed platypus, a flying fish and a mermaid. He was taking these strange creatures to England to the Museum of Natural History.

WRITER THREE Is there such a thing as a duck-billed platypus? A flying fish? If so, describe them.

GRANDFATHER As I recall the story, your great-grandmother said Dr. Griffin agreed to display all these strange creatures, including the mermaid, at the American Museum for a week before he went to England.

WRITER FOUR Who was the owner of The American Museum in 1842? What other exhibits might one see in the museum?

MARTHA Your great-grandmother must have been excited at the chance to see a real mermaid.

GRANDMOTHER Oh, she was so excited she couldn't sleep the night before. There were full-page ads in all the New York papers showing this beautiful young woman with a fish tail instead of legs.

MARTHA Did she really get to see it?

GRANDMOTHER Oh, yes. But she was a mite disappointed.

MARTHA It wasn't really a mermaid?

GRANDMOTHER Oh, it was a mermaid, all right. But it wasn't a beautiful woman like the ads showed. Great-grandmother said she saw a withered body of a monkey with the dried tail of a fish. It was the ugliest thing she had ever seen.

GRANDFATHER (Laughing) It was after that she got a bigger disappointment when she went to see the Egress!

MARTHA What kind of an animal is that? I never heard of an Egress.

GRANDMOTHER Neither had great-grandmother. She just followed a sign that said "This way to the Egress." That's when she found out what an Egress was.

WRITER FIVE Tell what an egress is.

____

MARTHA Did Dr. Griffin take the mermaid to England? Is it in a museum there now?

GRANDMOTHER No. The owner of the American Museum had it on exhibit for a month and then took it on a tour of the country.

GRANDFATHER I remember reading that after he brought it back, the Museum burned down and the mermaid with it.

GRANDMOTHER But you can see one just like it today at the Peabody Museum.

MARTHA If it's a real mermaid then how come so few people know about it?

SUPER RESEARCH CHALLENGE

WRITER SIX Is the Peabody Museum's mermaid at Harvard University real or not? Explain.

THE FEEJEE MERMAID

ADDITIONAL READING

The Lighthouse Mermaid by Kathleen Karr. Hyperion, 1998.
Kate dreams of mermaids, but can she face a hard task in the real world?

Little Mermaid by Hans Christian Andersen, adapted by D. Hautzig. Random House, 1991.
A retelling of the tale of the mermaid who falls in love with a prince.

Mermaid of Cafur by Evelyn Foster. Barefoot Books, 1999.
Is the mermaid real or a figment of the imagination?

Mermaid Summer by M. Hunter. HarperColins, 1988.
Anna discovers the secret means to undo a mermaid's curse on her grandfather.

Mermaid Tales from Around the World by M. Osborne. Scholastic, 1999.
Twelve mermaid tales from around the world retold and illustrated.

Monsters of the Deep by S. Pirotta. Raintree, 1996.
Explore the underwater world and learn about sharks, whales, mysterious sea serpents and more.

Monsters of the Deep by S. Ross. Lerner, 1998.
A dive into the dangerous waters of the world to discover the dangerous creatures that live there.

Sea Animals by Dorling Kindersley editors. Dorling Kindersley, 1992.
Color photographs and descriptions of animals that live in the sea.

Sea Creatures with Many Arms by D. Souza. Lerner, 1998.
A look at different sea creatures with multiple arms.

1842 THE FEEJEE MERMAID

Bondeson, Jan. **The Feejee Mermaid and Other Essays in Natural and Unnatural History**. Cornell University Press, 1999.

Early, Andrea. "**The Little Mermaid?**" Harvard University Gazette. Oct. 17, 1996.

1859 STREETS OF SILVER?

The rumor that was passed from one gold seeker to another in the 1860s was that the streets Virginia City, Nevada, were paved with silver. Was there any truth to the rumor?

Reading Parts Narrator One, Narrator Two, Peter O'Riley, Pat McLaughlin, Editor, Samuel Clemens

NARRATOR ONE On the 22nd of November, 1859, and for three days after, six feet of snow fell on Virginia City isolating the town from the rest of the world. It marked the beginning of a hard winter for the gold seekers who lived in canvas tents and brush shanties. Cattle were dying of cold and hunger. The people were hungry. One group of hardy prospectors found shelter at the mouth of a tunnel.

PETER O'RILEY We sure were lucky to find this place. It's a sight warmer than those brush shanties.

PAT MC LAUGHLIN And a good thing, too. There's not a nut pine tree standing anywhere in Six Mile Canyon or on Gold Hill either. Even the stumps were dug up for fuel.

PETER O'RILEY Sure seems like it ought to be getting light.

PAT MC LAUGHLIN We just woke up early. Maybe today will be the day we strike it rich. I thought I saw some interesting looking rock yesterday at the head of the ravine. It could turn out to be our own Sutter's Mill.

WRITER ONE What was important about Sutter's Mill in California? Tell what happened there in 1848.

____

____

____

PETER O'RILEY Something's not right. It's too dark. I'll go have a look outside.

NARRATOR TWO Peter made his way to the mouth of the tunnel to see if he could find any sign of daylight. It was black as pitch when he reached the entrance and ran right into a wall of snow.

PETER O'RILEY An avalanche! We've been buried. Grab your shovels.

WRITER TWO Explain what an avalanche is. Tell what causes an avalanche and what is most dangerous about an avalanche.

____

____

____

NARRATOR ONE His shout awakened the rest of the men who luckily had their shovels with them. In candlelight they began to dig, and in less than an hour had dug their way out. Not only was the sun shining, but in the canyon the snow was beginning to melt away.

PETER O'RILEY Let's go, Pat. I have a feeling that today we're going to make that strike.

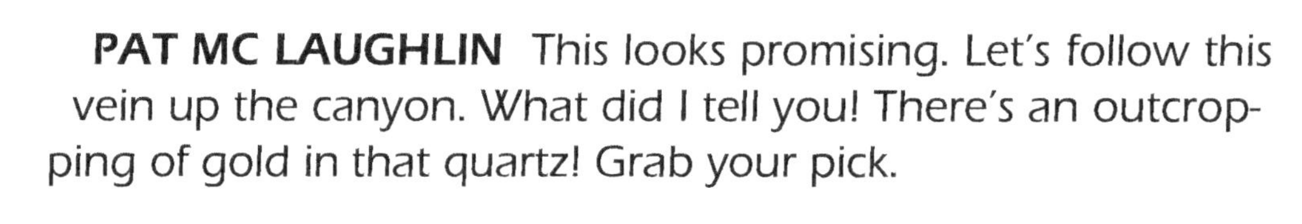

PAT MC LAUGHLIN This looks promising. Let's follow this vein up the canyon. What did I tell you! There's an outcropping of gold in that quartz! Grab your pick.

PETER O'RILEY This digging would be a mite easier without this mud. Sticks to the shovel like glue.

WRITER THREE Describe placer mining used in the early days of mining gold by prospectors.

____

____

____

PAT MC LAUGHLIN Dump these buckets in the rocker. Let's see what's left when we wash the dirt away. You're right. That blue-gray mud sticks to the rocker, too. But look there in the bottom scattered in that black rock.

PETER O'RILEY Is it real or is it fool's gold? Too bad we don't have Jenny Wimmer and her lye kettle handy.

PAT MC LAUGHLIN I never heard of Jenny Wimmer. What does she have to do with gold?

WRITER FOUR Visit this web site:
http://www.museumca.org/goldrush/ar08.html
Read the story about Jenny Wimmer and her lye kettle. Summarize the story.

____

____

____

NARRATOR TWO For weeks Peter O'Riley and Pat McLaughlin dug down in the blue-gray mud, washing the gold out of it and throwing the mud and black rock away. In July the diggings were visited by August Harrison who took a piece of the strange-looking black rock and had it examined (assayed) by an expert. The prospectors were throwing away a solid mass of silver.

NARRATOR ONE The rush for wealth began with adventurers from everywhere descending on the steep mountains where runaway wagons were a frequent sight. One scraggly, dusty miner showed up at the office of the daily *Territorial Enterprise* looking for a job as a reporter.

EDITOR I can't say you look much like a professional man. What experience have you had?

SAMUEL CLEMENS I've been a printer's apprentice and a Mississippi River pilot. Served with a Southern group during the Civil War and wrote a "History of a Campaign That Failed."

EDITOR What name do you go under?

SAMUEL CLEMENS My real name is Sam Clemens, but I go by the name, Mark Twain.

WRITER FIVE What famous mining camp story did Mark Twain publish in 1865? What later writings is Mark Twain best known for?

____

____

____

____

____

SAMUEL CLEMENS The first story I'd like to write is about that rascal Henry Comstock. When he stumbled on O'Reilly's and McLaughlin's find he claimed it was on his property and the gullible fools believed him.

EDITOR Those two did all right. They were taking out gold at the rate of a thousand dollars a day before Comstock made his claim. There's still plenty of gold and silver to be had for those who don't mind hard work.

SAMUEL CLEMENS And for any who can stand the noise. You can hear the engines, the clanking of the stamp mills, and the whistles going 24 hours a day.

EDITOR But Virginia City can lay claim to being the only city in the country with streets paved with silver.

SAMUEL CLEMENS Now that's a hoax to attract more settlers.

EDITOR But it's true. The mills aren't very good at getting all the silver and gold out of the rock, so some of that silver-bearing rock was used in building our main roads.

SAMUEL CLEMENS They look like any other roads to me.

EDITOR Maybe so. But I guarantee you, there's silver in the rocks underneath.

SUPER RESEARCH CHALLENGE

WRITER SIX Visit this web site.
http://dmla.clan.lib.nv.us/docs/nsla/archives/myth/myth41.htm
Retell the legend of how Virginia City got its name.

STREETS OF SILVER?

ADDITIONAL READING

Gold and Silver, Silver and Gold by Alvin Schwartz. Farrar, 1988.
A collection of rich lore and legends, facts and myths about these precious metals.

Gold Fever by C. McMorrow. Random House, 1996.
Beginning with the discovery of gold at Sutter's Mill and recounting the wild days when gold fever gripped the nation.

Gold in the Hills by L. Lawler. Pocket Books, 1995.
Left with relatives while their father goes gold hunting, two children strike up a friendship with a recluse.

Gold Miners of the Wild West by J. Savage. Enslow, 1995.
Profiles of some of the pioneers who traveled west in search of gold.

Gold Rush by Bobbie Kalman. Crabtree, 1998.
Learn about prospector's tools, gold rush towns, and the excitement of hitting "pay dirt."

Gold Rush Prodigal by B. Thoene. Bethany House, 1991.
A young man siezes the promise of a great future only to lose it all in the California gold rush.

The Great American Gold Rush by Rhoda Blumberg. Bradbury, 1989.
A comprehensive look at the people and events that were part of the gold rush of 1849.

Comstock Lode by Louis L'Amour. Bantam, 1980.
A family travels from England to seek its fortune in the gold fields.

Mark T-W-A-I-N by David Collins. Creative Minds, 1993.
Covers the life of the writer from his childhood to his career as a reporter, novelist and humorist.

Mark Twain: Great American Short Stories. Edited by P. Hill. American Guidance Services, 1998.
Five tales from a master storyteller.

1859 STREETS OF SILVER?

Axon, Gordon. **The California Gold Rush**. Mason/Charter, 1976.
Beebe, Lucius. **Comstock Commotion**. Stanford University Press, 1954.
Hinkle, Warren. **The Richest Place on Earth: The Story of Virginia City**. Houghton-Mifflin, 1978.
James, Ronald M. **The Roar and the Silence: A History of Virginia City and the Comstock lode**. University of Nevada, 1998.

1869 THE CARDIFF GIANT

A ten-and-a-half-foot tall fossilized man was unearthed on an upstate New York farm in 1869, and is on display today at the Farmer's Museum in Cooperstown, New York. Is it real or a hoax?

Reading Parts Farmer Newell, Essie Newell, Narrator, Farmhand One, Farmhand Two, Mr. Hull

NARRATOR The scene is a small farm in upper New York State near the town of Cardiff. The year is 1869.

FARMER NEWELL Essie, Essie, come right now! You won't rightly believe what the well diggers found.

ESSIE NEWELL William, I can't just leave my kitchen to see some fool thing some settler buried years ago. My bread just went into the oven.

WRITER ONE What was one of the first settlements in upper New York state?

____

____

____

____

FARMER NEWELL Wasn't no settler buried this. Essie, you got to come and see it.

ESSIE NEWELL I don't care if it's been in the ground since the Indians were here. I expect it can wait till my bread is baked.

WRITER TWO What Indian tribes lived in upper New York state in the 1700s? What artifacts from the tribes might have been unearthed 150 years later?

____

____

____

NARRATOR When Essie finally took the golden brown loaves out of the oven, she wiped her hands on her apron and made her way to the upper field where her husband and other farmhands were frantically digging. When they had competely uncovered the object, they stood back in awe.

FARMER NEWELL A giant, a real giant! If I didn't see it with my own eyes I wouldn't believe it.

ESSIE NEWELL Look at that. Poor thing, it's all twisted like it died hurting.

FARMHAND ONE Must have been his stomach. Look how he's grabbing it with his right hand.

FARMHAND TWO Look, you can still see the blue veins running up his arms.

ESSIE NEWELL Looks mighty old. Still got fingernails even if they are yellow. How big do you suppose it is, William?

FARMER NEWELL At least 10 or 11 feet. I've heard of fossils, but I never expected to find one this big.

FARMHAND ONE Remember what happened on Van Loon's farm about six months back?

FARMHAND TWO Sure do. He dug up some fossil bones that were a million years old. It was in all the papers.

WRITER THREE What is a fossil? How do fossils form? How can scientists determine the age of a fossil?

____

____

____

FARMHAND ONE Then this giant must be a million years old, too.

FARMHAND TWO I reckon so.

ESSIE NEWEL Just this past Sunday Pastor Barnes was preaching that giants once walked the Earth. I reckon this is one of them. Maybe you should ride to town and tell him about it.

FARMER NEWELL We should get my cousin, George Hull, down here. He can tell us if it's real. He's studied archeology and paleontology for years.

WRITER FOUR What is an archeologist? What is a paleontologist?

____

____

____

NARRATOR George Hull was contacted and arrived at the Newell farm within a few days.

MR. HULL There is no doubt that this is one of the greatest discoveries of all time.Greater even than Goliath.

ESSIE NEWELL The preacher talked about David and Goliath last Sunday. But he didn't say exactly how big Goliath was.

WRITER FIVE Was Goliath taller or shorter than the Cardiff Giant?

____

____

____

MR. HULL Get as many men as you can to excavate the area around the giant.

NARRATOR Word of mouth spread news of the stone giant from farm to farm and to nearby towns. Dirt roads surrounding the farm were soon dotted with wagonloads of neighbors who wanted to see the curiosity.

FARMER NEWELL Essie, we got ourselves a gold mine here. I'll get the boys to help me put up a tent around the grave and charge twenty-five cents a look.

ESSIE NEWELL Maybe folks waiting in line would want lemon-ade and sugar cookies.

FARMER NEWELL You could charge as much as ten cents. Maybe fifteen cents if it was summertime. The giant will make us a fortune!

NARRATOR On October 17th, 1869, the *Syracuse Journal* printed news of the discovery.

FARMER NEWELL Essie, the Stage Coach Company wants to make four trips a day to bring folks to see the giant. We can raise the price to fifty cents.

ESSIE NEWELL My goodness, look at all those folks. That fellow looks like a clergyman.

FARMER NEWELL And there's two college professors and real scientists come to look. One told me it was a real human giant turned to stone. Another one said he didn't believe it but that it was a statue built by some civilization thousands of years ago.

MR. HULL William, this is all well and good having wagonloads of folks come out here, but think what all this tramping around will do to your farm. You won't have a crop left to harvest.

FARMER NEWELL But this stone fellow sure is a moneymaker.

MR. HULL That's true right now, but what happens when all the folks around have seen him? I know a group of men in Syracuse who will pay $30,000 for the rights to exhibit the giant. They'll put him on display in a large exhibition hall. That way more than the local folks can see him.

ESSIE NEWELL I'd have to make a lot of lemonade and sugar cookies to take in $30,000.

FARMER NEWELL You're right. We'll sell a two-thirds interest in the giant if they pay to dig him up.

MR. HULL No problem there. He'll be the most talked about exhibit in the nation.

SUPER RESEARCH CHALLENGE

WRITER SIX Was the Cardiff Giant a real fossilized man or was it a hoax?

____

____

____

____

THE CARDIFF GIANT

ADDITIONAL READING

Cardiff Hill Mystery by J. Lorimer. Globe, 1984.
Beth inherits a cottage in the country and a lot of trouble to go with it.

Giant Bones by Patricia Beagle. New American Library, 1997.
Six short stories dealing with giants and other strange creatures.

Giant Humanlike Beasts by B. Innes. Raintree, 1999.
Do living links to Neanderthals still inhabit the planet? DNA evidence begs questions.

Giants in the Land by D. Applebaum. Houghton-Mifflin, 1993.
A look at the power of nature and the drive of human technology.

Hoaxers and Hustlers by T. Streissguth. Oliver Press, 1998.
This book will leave readers shaking their heads in amazement and disbelief.

New York by V. Schomp. Morning Glory Press, 1997.
Explore the unique character of New York state through its land, cultural diversity and stories of success.

New York by A. Gelman. Lerner, 1992.
Introduces the geography, history and people of New York state.

New York by D. Fradin. Children's Press, 1993.
Quick reference on the history, geography and population of the State of New York.

Strange Mysteries from Around the World by Seymour Simon. Morrow, 1997.
Unsolved mysteries that science cannot answer.

Strange Unsolved Mysteries of People and Places by P. Emert. Tor Publishers, 1992.
A collection of unanswered questions from the past to today's headlines.
University of Nevada, 1998.

1869 THE CARDIFF GIANT

Ross, Irwin. "**The Cardiff Giant Hoax**." American History Illustrated. 1968. 3(5): 38-41
Sears, Stephen W. "**The Giant in the Earth**." American Heritage, 1975. 26(5):94-99
Franco, Barbara. "**The Cardiff Giant: A Hundred Year Old Hoax**." New York History 1969. 50(4) 421-440

1935 ALLIGATORS IN THE SEWERS

Wealthy New Yorkers who wanted to escape the ice and snow of winter often vacationed in Florida. Many brought back baby alligators as pets, but when the alligators began to grow and snap at those who came near, something had to be done. The legend says that these beasts were flushed down toilets to get rid of them. Did they survive and reproduce in New York City sewers? Are there alligators living in the sewers today?

Reading Parts Narrator, Salvatore Condulcci, age 16, Frankie Lorenzo, age 19, Jimmy Mireno, age 19

NARRATOR It is the middle of the Great Depression and many people are out of work despite the efforts of the President and Congress to control the economy and find work for millions of jobless.

WRITER ONE Who was President of the United States in 1935? What was the New Deal? How was it supposed to help people?

____

____

____

____

NARRATOR The date is February 9th, 1935. The snows had been heavy in New York City, and two teenagers were busy shoveling snow to a third youth whose job it was to push it down a manhole.

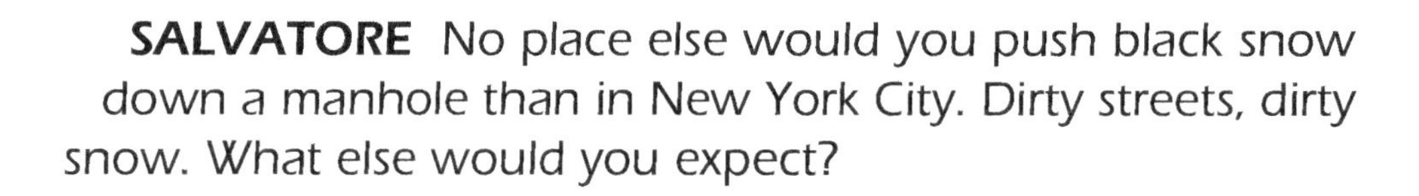

SALVATORE No place else would you push black snow down a manhole than in New York City. Dirty streets, dirty snow. What else would you expect?

JIMMY Watch out, Salvatore, here comes the last heap. I don't know why we have to clear the streets. That's what the WPA is for.

WRITER TWO What was the WPA? Why was it established? What were some of the jobs that WPA workers did?

____

____

____

____

SALVATORE Hey, you guys, wait a minute. Something's clogging the manhole.

FRANKIE Let me see. Something is moving down there.

JIMMY You're right. It's black and it's big!

SALVATORE Look again! It's crawling through the slush. It's an alligator!

FRANKIE Quit your kidding. I've heard those "alligator in the sewers" stories before. There's nothing to them.

JIMMY Oh, yeah? Salvatore's right. It is an alligator. See for yourself.

NARRATOR As the boys leaned over the manhole with heads bent low, they saw a live alligator threshing about in the ice trying to get clear.

SALVATORE Let's help it. Go find a rope. I'll make a slip knot and dangle it in the sewer. Then I can grab it when it gets close.

NARRATOR Two of the boys borrowed a rope from the Lehigh Stove and Repair Shop. Salvatore made a slip knot and dangled the noose into the sewer. After several misses he managed to get the rope around the gator's neck. The others grabbed the rope and all pulled. Slowly the animal was dragged to the street.

WRITER THREE Describe a medium-size Florida alligator.

____

____

____

____

JIMMY Salvatore, you sit on his tail while I get the rope off.

FRANKIE Move, guys! Can't you see he has his jaws open? One snap of those teeth and you can lose an arm.

SALVATORE Grab the snow shovels. Hit him on the head.

FRANKIE Wait! He's not moving. I think he's dead. Let's drag it down to the repair shop.

NARRATOR The boys took their eight-foot-long victim to the Lehigh Stove and Repair Shop where there was much speculation as to how it had gotten in the sewers.

FRANKIE It couldn't have escaped from a pet shop. There's no pet shop within miles of here.

JIMMY Maybe it fell off a passing steamer. You see boats all the time going past 123rd Street.

SALVATORE Or maybe its one of the alligators that live in the city sewers. I've heard there are hundreds of them down there. Some are blind with white skin. It's the darkness that does it to them.

NARRATOR This headline appeared in the *New York Times*, February 10, 1935. "Alligator Found in Uptown Sewer. Youths Shoveling Snow Into Manhole Snare It and Drag It Out. Whence It Came Is A Mystery."

WRITER FOUR What other headlines (major news events) appeared in the *New York Times* in 1935? Name at least three.

____

____

____

SUPER RESEARCH CHALLENGE

WRITER FIVE This play is based on true events as stated in the newspaper headlines of February 10, 1935. Which theory do you believe concerning the origin of the alligator? Are there really alligators in New York City sewers?

____

____

____

____

____

ALLIGATORS IN THE SEWERS
ADDITIONAL READING

Alligators and Crocodiles by E. Stoops. Child's World, 1996.
See how to tell the creatures apart, what they eat, how they live and why they eat only 50 times a year.

Alligators and Others All Year Long by Crescent Dragonwagon. Simon & Schuster, 1997.
A dozen poems that celebrate wildlife and the seasons.

Alligators: Life in the Wild by M. Kulling. Golden/Western, 2000.
Find out about alligators and their lives.

Franklin D. Roosevelt by A. Osinski. Children's Press, 1987.
The life and career of the 32nd president of the United States.

Franklin D. Roosevelt, The Four Term President by M. Schuman. Enslow, 1996.
Biography of the 32nd president from childhood to presidency.

Franklin Delano Roosevelt by Russell Freedman. Houghton-Mifflin, 1990.
A vivid photobiography of the president who guided the nation through the Depression and World War II.

New York by C. Hat. Creative Education, 2000.
Captures the character of New York City by exploring the past and investigating what the future may hold.

New York City by D. Kent. Chilldren's Press, 1996.
The history and people of New York City with color photographs.

New York Subway System by T. McNeese. Greenhaven Press, 1997.
Story behind the enqineering and construction of the subways.

Underground by David Macauley. Houghton-Mifflin, 1976.
A detailed look at the intricate support systems beneath large cities.

The Witch of Fourth Street by M. Levoy. Harcourt, 1972.
Stories about Lower East Side New York in the early 20th century.

1935 ALLIGATORS IN THE SEWERS

Brunvand, Jan H. **Too Good To Be True: The Colosssal Book of Urban Legends**. Norton, 1999.

Coleman, Loren. "**Alligators-in-the-Sewers: A Journalistic Origin**." Journal of American Folklore. 92(1979). 335-338

Dorson, Richard M. **America in Legend**. Pantheon, 1973.

RESEARCH CHALLENGES

1730 THE WITCH TRIAL AT MOUNT HOLLY

Writer One Over 20 men and women were accused of being witches. The penalty for witchcraft was hanging.

Writer Two A colonial woman's typical dress was made of dark homespun, sometimes with white trimming. Skirts were long and full. Sleeves were long. On the head was a white mob cap. Wealthy women imported dresses from England made of silk and satin and worn with hoops.

Writer Three Tests for witches included weighing on a scale opposite a Bible and being thrown in water. If one sank, one could not be a witch.

Writer Four The editor of the *Pennsylvania Gazette* was Benjamin Franklin "The Witch Trial at Mount Holly" was a hoax. It was a product of Franklin's imagination and was a satirical look at the numerous citizens of that time who still believed witches existed.

1730 THE GHOSTLY DRUMMER OF TEDWORTH

Writer One The first library in Philadelphia was established by Benjamin Franklin who is also credited with the first eye glasses, fire department, and central heating.

Writer Two In March, 1661, John Mompesson of Tedworth (England) brought a lawsuit against a local drummer. The man was found guilty and his drum was given to Mompesson. Soon afterwards Mompreson found that an angry drumming spirit had invaded his house.

Writer Three The publisher of The *Pennsylvania Gazette* was Benjamin Franklin. Another of his famous hoaxes was the reporting of a nonexistent "Witch Trial at Mount Holly."

1775 THE GHOST OF THE BOSTON MASSACRE

Writer One A typical house in Boston in 1770 was a 14- by 16-foot cottage with walls of rough-hewn timbers, a brick chimney and a thatched or shingled roof. Heavy wooden shutters were used instead of glass window panes.

Writer Two A colonial woman's typical dress was made of dark homespun, sometimes with white trimming. Skirts were long and full. Sleeves were long. On the head was a white mob cap. Wealthy women imported dresses from England made of silk and satin and worn with hoops.

Writer Three The presence of British troops in the city had aroused great anger among the citizens of Boston. The riot began when 50 to 60 persons attacked a British sentinel. Captain Preston, a British officer, brought several men to his assistance. The crowd attacked these soldiers also. The soldiers fired into the crowd, killing three persons and wounding eight, two of whom died later.

Writer Four Redcoats carried muskets 6-7 feet long which fired round balls loaded from the muzzle. A paper held the explosive charge. Soldiers stood in parallel lines and fired at the enemy. Muskets were inaccurate beyond 100 yards.

Writer Five The engraving of the Boston Massacre shows Redcoats standing in a line in the streets of Boston firing at a group of colonists. Several colonists are wounded, others are retreating. Smoke from the guns fills the air. One Redcoat raises his sword. Colonists do not appear to have muskets.

Writer Six Answers will vary.

Writer Seven Answers will vary.

Writer Eight The British did not stand in a straight line and shoot. It was a mixed-up free-for all. One would not see a blue sky after nine o'clock in a winter night. There is no ice or snow on the streets as there should be. Crispus Attacks, the first black man to die in the Revolution, is shown as white.

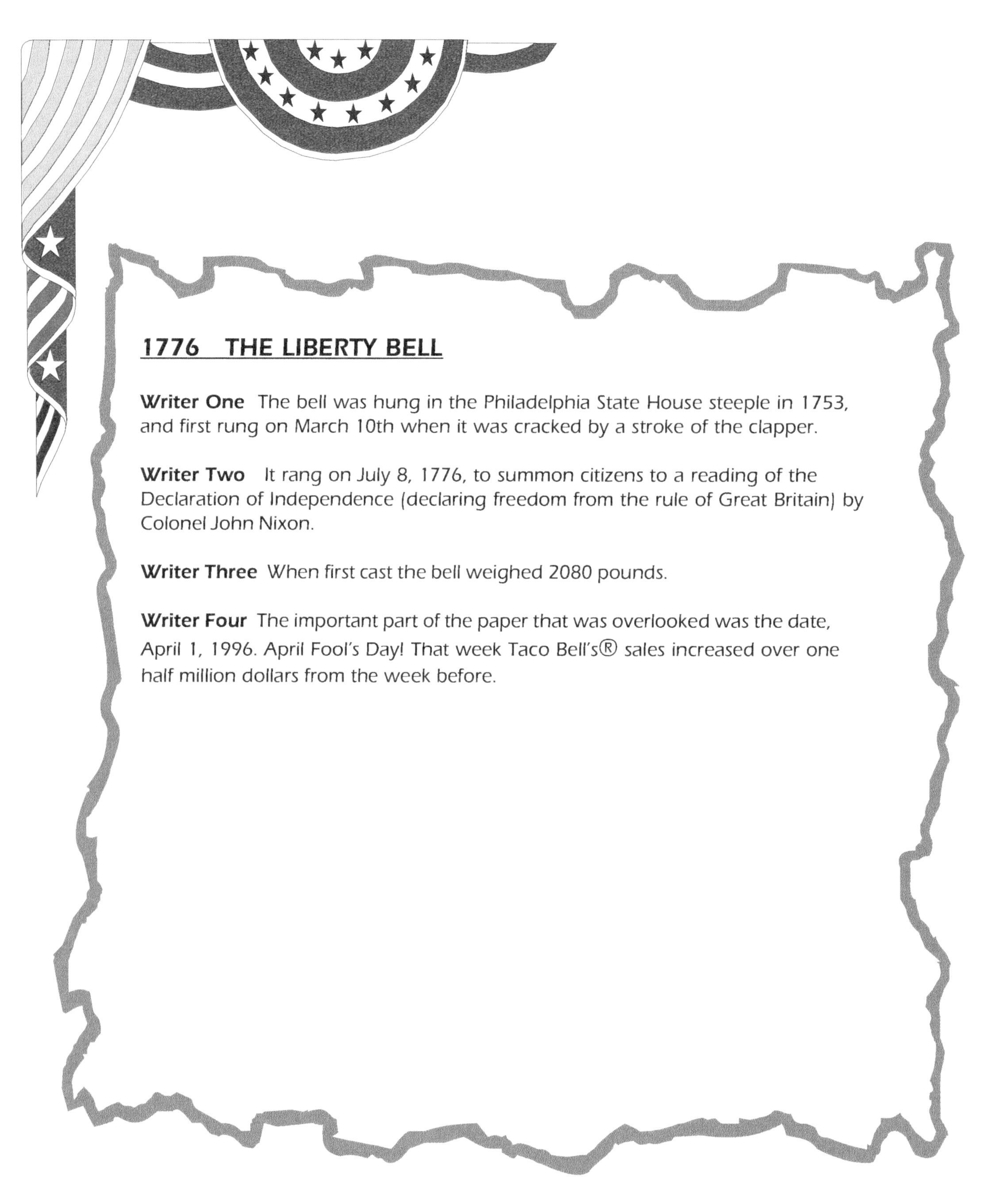

1776 THE LIBERTY BELL

Writer One The bell was hung in the Philadelphia State House steeple in 1753, and first rung on March 10th when it was cracked by a stroke of the clapper.

Writer Two It rang on July 8, 1776, to summon citizens to a reading of the Declaration of Independence (declaring freedom from the rule of Great Britain) by Colonel John Nixon.

Writer Three When first cast the bell weighed 2080 pounds.

Writer Four The important part of the paper that was overlooked was the date, April 1, 1996. April Fool's Day! That week Taco Bell's® sales increased over one half million dollars from the week before.

1817 THE GLOUCESTER SEA SERPENT

Writer One Gloucester, Massachusetts, is an important fishing center in Northeast Massachusetts. It is near the tip of Cape Ann and about 30 miles from Boston. The well-protected harbor is ideal for ships and in the 1700s and early 1800s the waters abounded with fish.

Writer Two Answers may vary. The Great Republic, a large sailing ship, weighed 555 tons, was 325 feet long, had 30 sails and a crew of 130 men.

Writer Three The Mosasaur was a giant swimming lizard up to 50 feet long that some felt might have survived the Cretaceous Period which saw the extinction of the dinosaurs. It had a long neck and a reptile-like head, similar to the descriptions given by witnesses.

Writer Four Elephant seals are 9-13 feet long and weigh more than 1000 pounds. They are found in the Pacific Ocean, and while they can stay under water 40 minutes, they have short necks and do not match the descriptions of witnesses. It had a long neck and a reptile-like head, similar to the descriptions given by witnessses. The anaconda can grow up to 60 feet in length with a 12-inch round body. It is unlikely that the anaconda could survive in the colder waters of the New England coast. It's natural habitat is the warm waters of the tropics.

Writer Five J. P. O'Neill, author of **The Great New England Sea Serpent,** theorizes that over-fishing of areas off the coast of Massachusetts has forced the sea serpent to look elsewhere for food, and that is the reason for so few sightings in the 20th century. Steps are being taken today to bring back the abundent fish that once swan off the Gloucester Coast. Perhaps with a rich feeding ground, the Glucester Sea Serpent will once again appear.

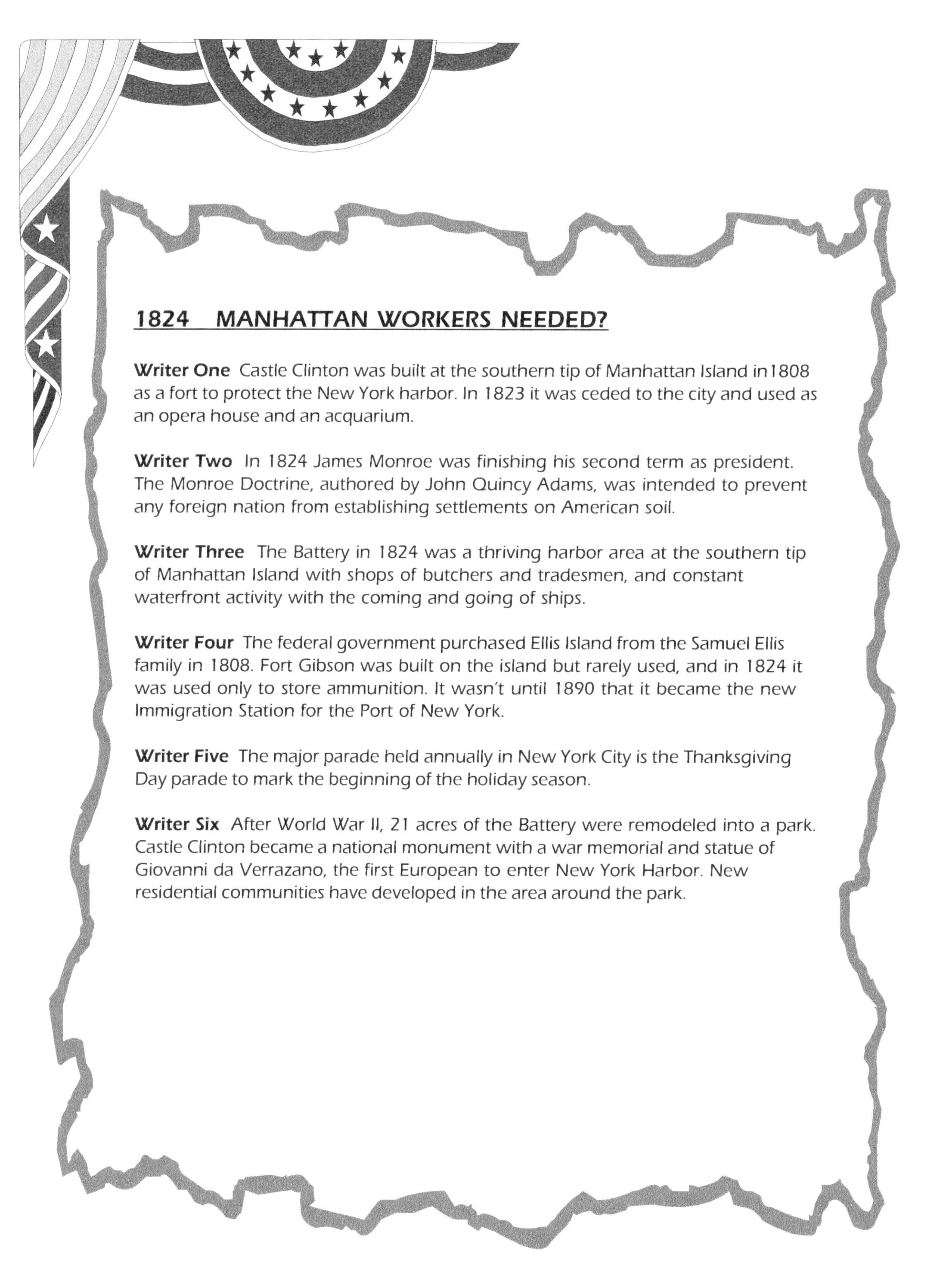

1824 MANHATTAN WORKERS NEEDED?

Writer One Castle Clinton was built at the southern tip of Manhattan Island in1808 as a fort to protect the New York harbor. In 1823 it was ceded to the city and used as an opera house and an acquarium.

Writer Two In 1824 James Monroe was finishing his second term as president. The Monroe Doctrine, authored by John Quincy Adams, was intended to prevent any foreign nation from establishing settlements on American soil.

Writer Three The Battery in 1824 was a thriving harbor area at the southern tip of Manhattan Island with shops of butchers and tradesmen, and constant waterfront activity with the coming and going of ships.

Writer Four The federal government purchased Ellis Island from the Samuel Ellis family in 1808. Fort Gibson was built on the island but rarely used, and in 1824 it was used only to store ammunition. It wasn't until 1890 that it became the new Immigration Station for the Port of New York.

Writer Five The major parade held annually in New York City is the Thanksgiving Day parade to mark the beginning of the holiday season.

Writer Six After World War II, 21 acres of the Battery were remodeled into a park. Castle Clinton became a national monument with a war memorial and statue of Giovanni da Verrazano, the first European to enter New York Harbor. New residential communities have developed in the area around the park.

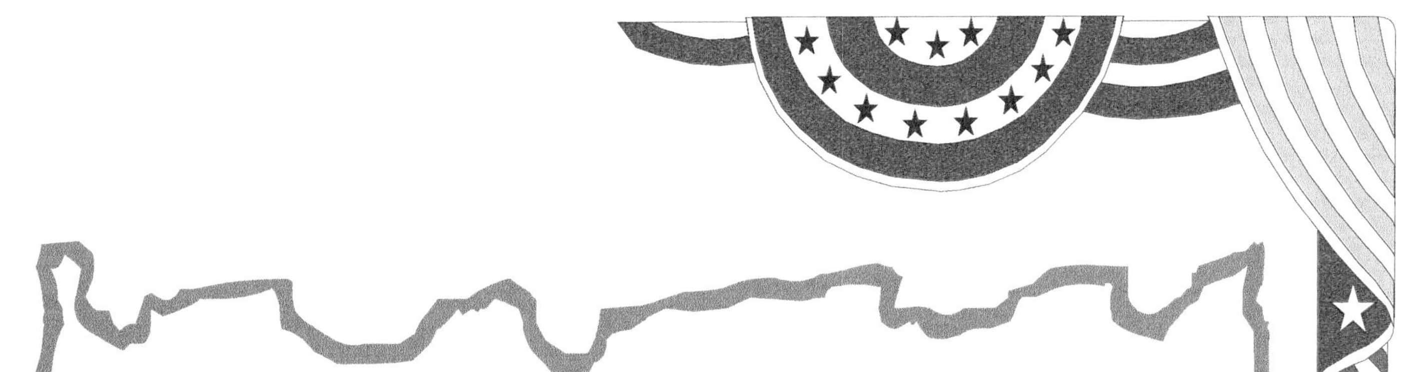

1835 JOICE HETH

Writer One P.T. Barnum was considered a master showman of his day. Born in 1810, he sold lottery tickets when he was 12 and by age 25 he began a career in exhibiting curiosities to the American public, including Joice Heth, the Feejee Mermaid and Tom Thumb. In 1841, he bought the American Museum in New York City where he exhibited "500,000 natural and artificial curiosities from every corner of the globe." He presented European opera star, Jenny Lind in 95 concerts. His name will forever be connected with the Barnum & Bailey Circus.

Writer Two Madagascar is the fourth largest island in the world. It lies 250 miles east of Africa. It has a coast of more than 3000 miles. In the 1600s the French attempted to establish settlements on the island but failed. It became a haven for pirates and slave traders who captured many of the island people and sold them as slaves to nearby islands and to the New World.

Writer Three Answers may vary.

Writer Four New York City April 30, 1789. With a tap tap of hammers banners go up all over New York City. On this day George Washington will become the first President of the United States. At Murrays Wharf great cheers go up, cannons explode, the smell of gunpowder is in the air. Church bells ring out as the Presidential barge approaches. Then George Washington, over six feet tall, dressed as plainly as a working man, ignores the waiting carriage and walks with the crowd. Washington and his party enter Federal Hall. The great man appears on the balcony above the crowd. Other important men are around him. He speaks the Oath of Office. "I will faithfully execute the Office of President to preserve, protect and defend the Constitution of the United States." A roaring cheer goes up. Again church bells ring.

Writer Five Joice Heth died on February 19, 1836. The doctor who performed the autopsy (at Barnum's request) certified that Joice Heth could not have been more than 80 years old at the time of her death. Obviously Barnum was sorry he had requested the autopsy, and to cover his embarrassment, planted a story in the *New York Herald* (February 27, 1836) that said the body that was autopsied was not that of Joice Heth.

1842 THE FEEJEE MERMAID

Writer One Hans Christian Andersen was a homely child who did not do well in school, suffered from poverty and neglect during his childhood, and when he was 14 years of age he ran away to Copenhagen. There he worked for Jonas Collin, director of the Royal Theater, until Collin raised money to provide him with an education.

Writer Two Haiti is an island in the Caribbean Sea. Columbus 's second voyage took him there in 1493. He found that men he had left on the island from his first voyage had all been killed by Indians.

Writer Three The fur-covered duck-billed platypus lives in Australia. Its muzzle is shaped like a duck's bill. It is about two feet long and weighs almost four pounds. Flying fish are found in all warm seas. They throw themselves from the water with the motion of their tails. Once in the air they spread large fins which act like the wings of a glider.

Writer Four Early in 1842, P. T. Barnum opened the American Museum on Broadway in New York. A modern cabinet of wonders, it displayed real minerals, fossils, and stuffed animals alongside the Feejee Mermaid.

Writer Five "Egress" means exit.

Writer Six The mermaid at the Peabody Museum was made by Southeast Asian fishermen by sewing together the head of a monkey and the tail of a fish. Others were made of papier-mache with the teeth, fingernails and fins being those of a carp.

1859 STREETS OF SILVER?

Writer One Gold was discovered at Sutter's Mill in California on January 24, 1848, by James Marshall, sawmill superintendent. This led to the greatest gold rush in the nation's history as the 49ers headed west in search of riches.

Writer Two An avalanche is a large mass of snow, ice, earth or rock in swift motion down a mountainside. An avalanche can be set off by loud noise or heavy motion that disturbs the snow or rock layer. Many lives have been lost and buildings demolished in avalanches.

Writer Three In the early days of placer mining men panned the gold by hand, swirling the water and gravel in a large pan, leaving the heavier gold at the bottom. Miners also used shovels to scoop the gravel into a sort of cradle, then rocked the cradle, washing and sifting out all the lighter materials until only the gold was left.

Writer Four When James Marshall found a gold nugget at Sutter's Mill in 1848, he wanted to know if it was real gold. He sent the nugget to Jenny Wimmer, the only woman at the camp who had ever seen a nugget of placer gold (from the time she panned for gold as a child in Georgia.) She declared the nugget to be gold and proved it by tossing it in her lye kettle. The nugget stayed in the lye overnight and came out as gold in the morning.

Writer Five Twain's famous mining camp story was "The Celebrated Jumping Frog of Calaveras County." Later well-known writings were **Tom Sawyer** and **Huckleberry Finn.**

Writer Six Legend says that an old prospector, James Finney, better known as Old Virginny, discovered part of the Comstock Lode in June, 1859. He sold his interest in his claim for an old horse and a pair of blankets. Going home one night he fell and the bottle in his hand broke. He said: "I baptize this ground Virginia Town." Later, the local miners in a meeting decided to name the town Virginia City.

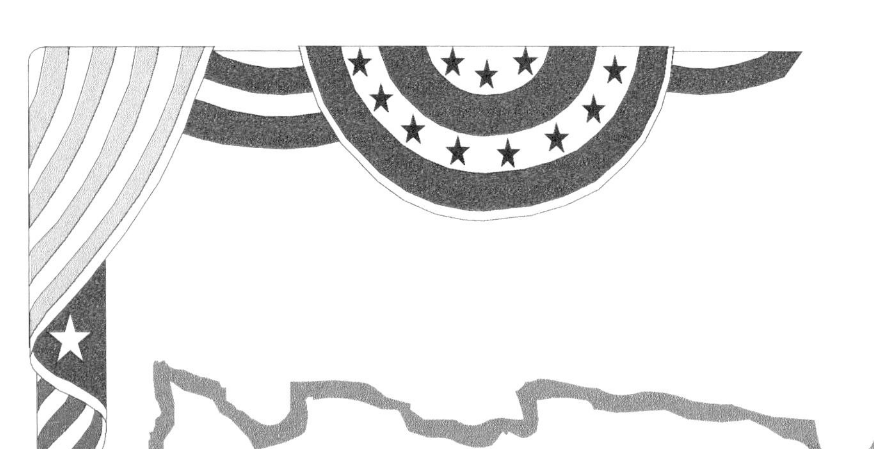

1869 THE CARDIFF GIANT

Writer One The first permanent settlement in upper New York state was in 1624. Fort Orange, now known as Albany, had 30 families.

Writer Two The Indian tribes settlers encountered were the Mohawk, Oneida, Onondaga, Cayuga, Seneca and Iroquois. They were farmers and hunters. Artifacts left by this tribe might include hoes made of wood, stone, bone or shell, arrowheads, bows, spears and clubs.

Writer Three Fossils are the remains of living things preserved in rock. Geologists date them by seeing which fossils are in different layers of rocks. The fossils in lower layers would be older than the fossils in the layers above.

Writer Four A paleontologist is someone who studies fossils. An archeologist studies ancient civilizations.

Writer Five Goliath, found in Biblical literature, is described as being nine and a half feet tall. He was killed by David with a stone from a slingshot. The Cardiff Giant was at least 11 feet tall.

Writer Six The Cardiff Giant was a hoax. George Hull had a giant carved out of stone, made to look old and transported to his cousin, William Newell's farm where it was buried and later "discovered." He sold rights to the giant to a Syracuse syndicate for $30,000 where it was displayed and attracted huge crowds. Even though experts declared it to be a humbug, it continued to be displayed and is found today in the Farmer's Museum in Cooperstown, New York.

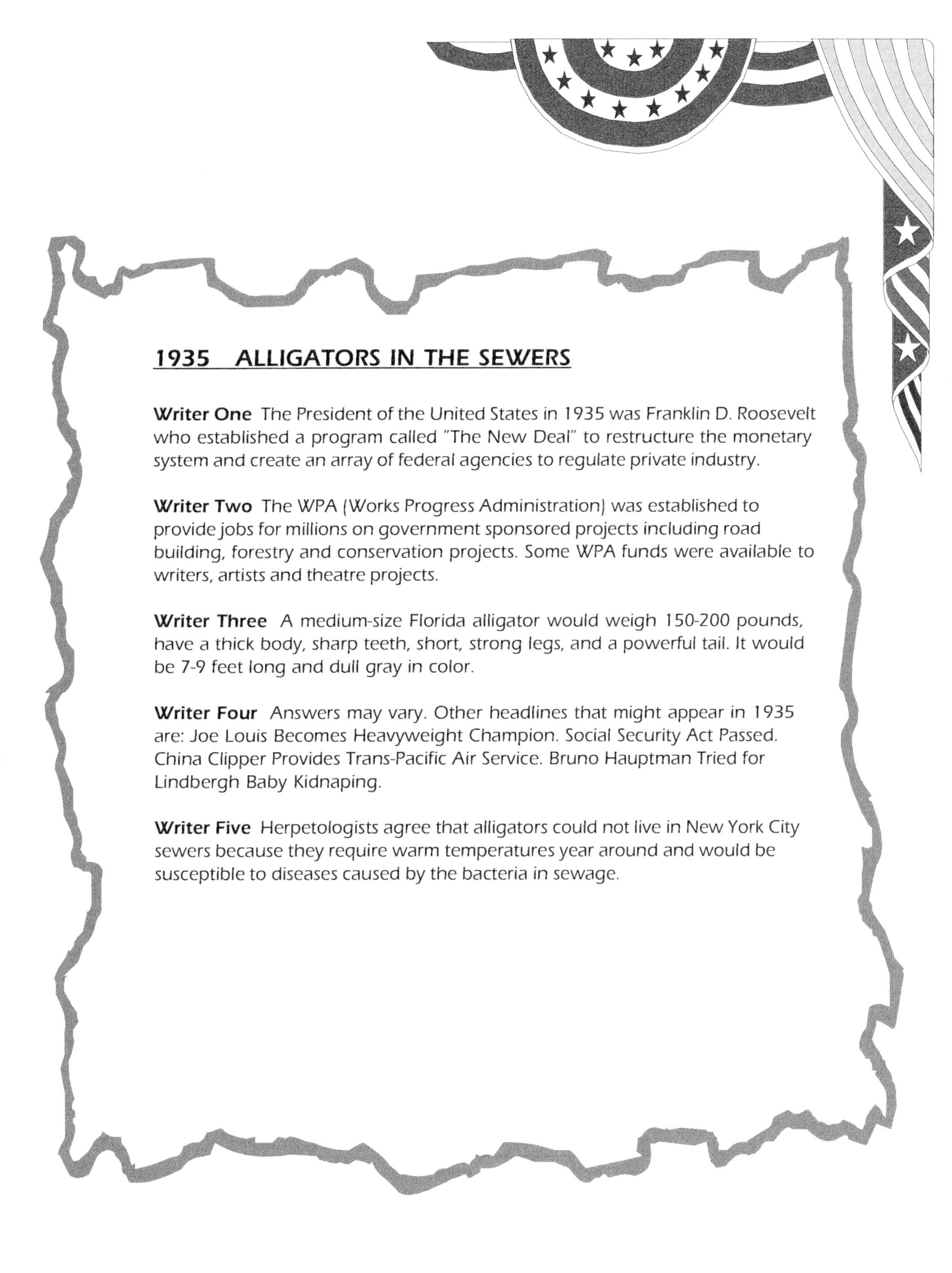

1935 ALLIGATORS IN THE SEWERS

Writer One The President of the United States in 1935 was Franklin D. Roosevelt who established a program called "The New Deal" to restructure the monetary system and create an array of federal agencies to regulate private industry.

Writer Two The WPA (Works Progress Administration) was established to provide jobs for millions on government sponsored projects including road building, forestry and conservation projects. Some WPA funds were available to writers, artists and theatre projects.

Writer Three A medium-size Florida alligator would weigh 150-200 pounds, have a thick body, sharp teeth, short, strong legs, and a powerful tail. It would be 7-9 feet long and dull gray in color.

Writer Four Answers may vary. Other headlines that might appear in 1935 are: Joe Louis Becomes Heavyweight Champion. Social Security Act Passed. China Clipper Provides Trans-Pacific Air Service. Bruno Hauptman Tried for Lindbergh Baby Kidnaping.

Writer Five Herpetologists agree that alligators could not live in New York City sewers because they require warm temperatures year around and would be susceptible to diseases caused by the bacteria in sewage.

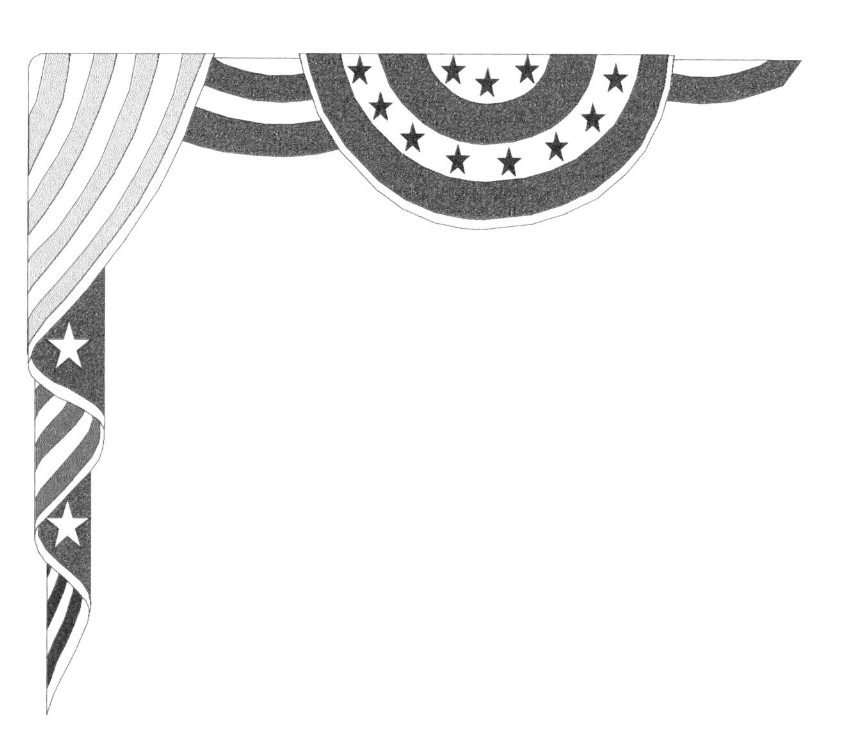

NOTES